Power Electronics in Motor Drives

Martin Brown

Elektor International Media BV
p.o box 11
6114 ZG Susteren
The Netherlands

British Library Cataloguing in Publication Data
A catalogue record for this book is available from the British Library

ISBN 978-0-905705-89-7

Prepress production: Hans van de Weijer
First published in the United Kingdom 2010
Printed in the Netherlands by Wilco, Amersfoort

109019-UK

Table of Contents

Introduction

This book is not about drive or power electronic theory. It is not about complex topologies, control algorithms, and stability criteria.
It is much more about the real world of AC drives designers and users. There are a few people who need to understand the complexities of motor simulation, but there are a great many more who want to understand the basic principles of AC drive design and operation, and who are interested in how they are used in the real industrial world.

This book is aimed at them, and at their engineering colleagues who are interested in, for example, quality control in a sugar mill, but need to know how their key equipment works. It should also be of interest to automation engineers and programmers who need to understand the possibilities and limitations of simple AC drives. I hope it will also appeal to those of you who have an interest in how industry utilises power electronic components and systems to produce the things that we need (or think we need) at a price and quality that we have come to expect.

AC drives are now dominant in general industrial applications, and this book focuses on simple drive applications, which are those encountered by most engineers. If you want to understand how a drive and motor work with a fan or conveyor, this book will help you; if you want to design a factory to make aluminium foil, you'd better look further.

Electronics is often described as a rapidly changing and complex subject. In fact, if we discount the blizzard of patents and research papers published every month, and look instead at commercially available products, we see that the basic components and circuitry in a power supply or drive have not changed for many years. What has changed is the price, size and efficiency of the components, as well as the complexity of the control software that has greatly improved the reliability and flexibility of all electronic systems. With the extensive use of computer-aided design, the packaging and cooling have also been greatly improved.

As a result, modern industrial electronics is smaller, lower cost and more versatile than older equipment, while still recognisable - at least in the visible components - to a designer of a previous generation like myself.

Users of drives need to understand the basic principles of how they work, but it is more important for them to understand how the equipment is used, and how it can benefit the user.

An important part of this book is therefore the description of the functions and applications of the drives, and how they interact with the plant and their equipment. The list of applications is not exhaustive, but is intended to illustrate the most common uses of the equipment. AC drives, for example are used in horse exercising machines, fairground rides, and hot tubs. However, a description of their application in conveyors, grinders and fans is of more use to most engineers, if not as entertaining.

I have included in the book a description of the basic components that are used in drives with particular reference to the practical aspects of their installation in industrial equipment. This is important, if only to understand what may happen when a capacitor dries out, or an inductor saturates. This equipment inevitably interacts with the power electronic systems and must be at least recognisable by any engineer on site.
Finally, I have kept the mathematics to a minimum. Some basic understanding of mechanical and electrical theory is presumed, and a basic knowledge of single and three phase AC systems would be useful.

This book is written from a European perspective, which works with a supply frequency of 50Hz. In most cases 60Hz can be substituted without losing meaning; where this is not the case, the difference is explained.

Enjoy!

About the Author

Martin Brown graduated from Leicester University and worked in power electronics, joining Siemens in 1981 where he developed several innovative, high voltage power supplies for use in the terrestrial side of satellite communications. In 1987 he worked with a small team to develop a low cost AC inverter drive to control the speed of industrial induction motors. It was a technical and commercial success! More drives soon followed and later Martin became involved with customer applications, visiting sites all around the world. He continued his travels as a trainer for service, sales and support personnel as well as customers. He visited customers' installations and plant, experiencing first hand just how drives are really used - and often abused. This insight, adding to his technical knowledge of the subject has culminated in a useful mass of experience. Martin retired from Siemens UK in 2009 and felt his knowledge and experience was worth sharing in this book. When he isn't writing, he enjoys classic motor cycles, walking and travelling.

Acknowledgements

Gordon Smith at Leicester University introduced me to power electronics and the real world of engineering. Ray Stanyard taught me to think and design practically and laterally at the same time. My colleagues at Siemens showed that a team of engineers is greater than the sum of its parts. All these people have contributed, without knowing, to my questionable capabilities as an engineer and trainer - my thanks to them. I'd particularly like to thank Richard Kenney for his careful proofreading and Paul Ridgway for his help and advice. Finally, my thanks to my wife Sheila for being there for so long.

1. You probably know this but

We'll go though it anyway. The following chapter is a quick revision of electrical, electronic and mechanical theory with particular, and practical reference to what comes later – Power electronics and drives.

Some Basic Equations

Ohms law and the Power law are still the basis of practically any engineering in electrical systems. It's amazing how they keep coming up and being used all the time. Even software engineers use them:

Ohms Law

Voltage/Current = Resistance
$V/I = R$; rearranging, we get $V = IR$ or $I = V/R$
(Voltage in Volts, Current in Amperes (Amps) and Resistance in Ohms)

Power Law

Voltage x Current = Power
$V \times I = P$

If we use Volts and Amps, then the power comes out nicely in Watts. In the US, power is still talked about as Horsepower, particularly for motors. One Horsepower is 746W; conveniently pretty much three quarters of a kilowatt, so a standard 7.5kW motor is pretty close to 10Hp.

If we substitute IR for V in the power equation we get:

$$P = I^2R$$

This is quite important. It means resistive losses in cables, motor windings etc. are proportional to the square of the current, and so in practice this means that if you overload a motor by 50%, you'll get more than double the losses.
It also means that if you are working at 115V instead of 230V, then for the same power you have double the current and you'll need four times the cable thickness or you must live with four times the losses. That's why power is transmitted at as high a voltage as possible and industry tends to work with 400V or more.

Components and Ohms Law

Resistance

Resistance is useless – well, it burns power at least. We use resistors all the time in electronic circuits for limiting current and setting a voltage using a potential divider. In power electronics we have to think a lot more about the dissipation of our big resistors, and how we'll cool them. Resistors that work at high DC voltages (600V DC and above) need a little care, as they can prove unreliable. Some resistors may not clear as an open circuit when they fail at high voltage, leading to a visit by the fire brigade to your customer. Not good for follow up sales!!

Impedance - Inductors

When we come to examine AC systems, we must understand the concept of impedance. Impedance is like resistance, but is lossless. Inductors have impedance to AC as the varying current creates a varying magnetic field. We'll see later how the magnetic field is affected by the presence of iron, but without the iron we have a nice linear relationship, an extension of Ohms law:

$$V = L \times di/dt$$

where L is the inductance in Henries, and di/dt the rate of change of current. Now, one of the nice things about sine waves is that when you differentiate or integrate them they just shift their phase a bit and become cosines. So for a sine wave signal we get a simpler relationship:

$$V = L \times \omega \times I$$

Where ω (Greek letter Omega) is the angular velocity (we'll come across this later in relation to mechanics, which also uses angular velocity), which is $2\pi f$, and f is the frequency of the sine wave.
So:

$$V = 2\pi fL \times I.$$

So the impedance of the inductor, the equivalent of the resistance in Ohms of a resistor, is

$$X_L = 2\pi fL$$

(X is often used to represent impedance, X_L for inductive impedance)

That is, the impedance of an inductor is directly proportional to the applied frequency. So in power engineering, an inductor of one millihenry (1mH) in a 50Hz supply will have an impedance, X, of:

$X_L = 2 \times 3.14 \times 50 \times 0.001$

$X_L = 0.314$ Ohms

The impedance at 1kHz is:

$X_L = 2 \times 3.14 \times 1000 \times 0.001$

$X_L = 6.28$ Ohms

Much higher! We'll see later why that makes an inductor an important component in power electronic systems. Remember, there is no loss here, only impedance. Of course, real inductors have windings, which have real, resistive losses and iron cores, which have magnetising losses.

So how about all this iron and ferrite in inductors? Air cored inductors are fine for low values of inductance in radios and things, but for power we need millihenries of inductance, and iron will store a lot more magnetic energy than air, so this reduces the number of turns and the amount of copper needed for a particular inductance.
Iron incurs losses as it is magnetised and demagnetised with an alternating current, and these losses increase with frequency, so high frequency inductors use low loss powered iron cores, special ferrites or other materials. At lower frequencies it is enough to use laminated steel cores that limit lossy currents (referred to as eddy currents, named after nobody) that are induced in the iron by the alternating magnetic field.

If an inductor is working with only AC and has enough iron in the core, that is no problem. However, if there's a DC component in the current, the magnetisation of the iron will build up and the core will saturate. That is, the core will become fully magnetised and it won't be able to store any more energy, causing the inductance to collapse. To avoid this, inductors used for DC have an air gap where the magnetic energy is concentrated. Air gaps, like air-cored inductors, tend to spread the magnetic field out a bit and can cause audible noise and EMC problems.

An air gap near a metal casing will not only induce eddy currents and losses in the metal, but will also cause the casing to hum at an annoying frequency such as 300Hz (360Hz with a 60Hz supply), which is the ripple frequency on a DC link derived from a three phase supply (See chapter 2).

Inductors are used in power supplies for energy storage and filtering, but drives engineers will often fit them between the mains and drive for several reasons (see chapter 4). So if you see something that looks like a transformer in the bottom of a cubicle, don't sell it for the scrap copper and iron price, it's probably there for a reason.
By the way, this inductor may also be called a choke, a commutation choke or a reactor, but it's all means the same thing.

Of course, if we put a second winding on an inductor, a voltage is induced in that winding, and we can take out the energy that was put in by the first winding, getting electrical isolation and voltage change at the same time. Now it's not an inductor any more, it's a transformer. Transformers usually work with AC, and therefore don't have air gaps,but we'll see in chapter 2 we can supply them from DC, providing we reset them somehow.

Where do all the names come from?
The units discussed in this book are named by and large after the men (yes, they're all men) who discovered them. If you're interested:

Count Alessandro Giuseppe Antonio Anastasio Volta was an Italian Physicist who in 1800 invented the battery; he was made a count by Napoleon.

André-Marie Ampère was French, another physicist, whose father was executed in the French revolution, and was instrumental in developing electromagnetism, demonstrating it to the French Academy 1820.

Georg Simon Ohm was a German physicist and teacher, who worked with the battery, and published a book in 1827 which explains Ohm's law, largely as we know it today.

James Watt was a Scottish mechanical engineer who improved Newcomen's steam engine; in the 1780's he got into the usual arguments about patents.

Joseph Henry was an American scientist and was the first secretary of the Smithsonian Institution. Working with an early DC motor, he discovered self inductance in the 1830's.

And later in this chapter we'll meet:
Michael Faraday was an English chemist and physicist who worked with Humphry Davy, did quite a lot of chemistry, and after a lot of experiments and evaluation, was able to demonstrate mutual induction in the 1830's.

James Prescott Joule was an English physicist and brewer, who discovered the relationship between heat and mechanical work in 1840, but was largely ignored for a time, maybe because he wasn't an academic.

Sir Isaac Newton needs no introduction, as he made major advances in physics, mathematics, astronomy; he was also into alchemy and religion, and took charge of the Royal Mint in 1699.

Impedance – Capacitors

Capacitors allow AC current to flow because they charge and discharge. They store energy electrostatically as a charge on adjacent plates of opposite polarity. Their impedance is expressed as a function of the rate of change of voltage and the current:

$dV/dt = I/C$

Again, for a sine wave voltage or current, we can use ω, or 2πf:

$V = I/(2\pi fC)$

So the impedance part, X_C, is

$X_C = 1/2\pi fC$

That is, for a given capacitance, the impedance reduces as the frequency increases. So a 50μF capacitor (F for Farad, named after Michael Faraday; big man, big unit, so we use microfarads: μF) has an impedance at 50Hz of:

$X_C = 1/(2 \times 3.14 \times 50 \times 50\times10^{-6})$
$X_C = 637$ Ohms

At 1kHz, this impedance becomes

$X_C = 31.8$ Ohms

At 1MHz, this impedance will be down to:

$X_C = 0.00628$ Ohms

Small capacitors are used to provide low impedance sources of supply in small signal electronics as well as for filtering, oscillators etc. But in power electronics you'll come across some big capacitors connected across the DC link that supplies the inverter part of an AC drive. They serve several purposes. They'll hold up the voltage for a few milliseconds in the event of a short supply dip. On drives fed by a single phase supply they are vital since otherwise the DC would drop to zero every half cycle.
When energy comes back from the motor, (we'll see later how and when this happens) they'll absorb some of it as the voltage on them rises.

Probably most importantly though, they offer a low impedance source and sink for currents that flow between the DC and the inverter at the output. There are Amps flying around here at hundreds of kilohertz, so the low impedance offered by the capacitors is vital.

Nearly all DC link capacitors are electrolytic. That is, they achieve a high capacitance value by using a liquid electrolyte in conjunction with the negative aluminium foil, and an oxide layer on the positive aluminium foil (which is etched to produce a very large surface area) as the dielectric. The oxide layer is produced by electrochemical action, and as a result, electrolytic capacitors are polarised; anything more than a few tenths of a volt in the reverse direction and they will fail. This isn't usually a problem with DC link capacitors, unless you connect them the wrong way round, and then they fail in spectacular fashion, with paper and foil all over the workshop. I speak, of course, from experience. Also, electrolytics are not ideal capacitors in that they have a series inductance and resistance. The inductance isn't too much of a problem, but you'll often see plastic capacitors in parallel with electrolytics to offer a low impedance at high frequencies. The resistance means that the capacitors are a bit lossy, and at the high currents and frequencies we encounter in power electronics – especially on the DC link of an AC drive – care must be taken to ensure some cooling is available. Spacing the capacitors out, using lots of small ones with greater surface area, or directing some of the forced air over them are typical solutions.

Finally, they have a limited life. This is usually calculated by the manufacturer on the basis of operating voltage, current and temperature. When all three are at the absolute limit, life may be reduced to as little as 1000 hours. However, with a bit of headroom on one or two of the parameters, life extends rapidly to an acceptable level. A lot of people get concerned about capacitor life, but failure due to old age is very unusual (in drives that is, not people). Also, failure is defined here as values moving out of specification, not necessarily catastrophic failure.

If a drive has been standing for a time (say 12 months or more) the DC link capacitors need reforming before they work properly; follow the manufacturer's instructions to apply voltage slowly and for a couple of hours before starting the drive, so to re-establish the oxide layer.

Despite these drawbacks, electrolytics remain the capacitor of choice for most DC power applications, basically, of course, because you get more Farad for your Pound, Euro or Dollar.

Energy storage with Inductors and Capacitors

So we have some very simple components that will give us impedance that increases with frequency (inductors), or decreases with frequency (capacitors). Very handy, but we also use them to store energy, most obviously with capacitors on the DC link. The energy stored in a capacitor can be shown to be

$$E = \frac{1}{2} CV^2$$

And for an inductor

$$E = \frac{1}{2} Li^2$$

So a 1000 μF capacitor on a 600V DC link stores 180 Joules of energy. Not a lot, but if you get your screwdriver across it, it seems like a lot. I speak from experience. Always check capacitors are fully discharged before working with them; they can hold their charge for a long time.
A 5mH inductor with 10A in it is storing 250 Joules – a bit more, but it's a bit bigger and heavier.
Try and break the flow of current and you'll draw a beautiful, burning, possibly lethal arc. The figure below shows how I'm drawing these components, and summarises the equations related to them.

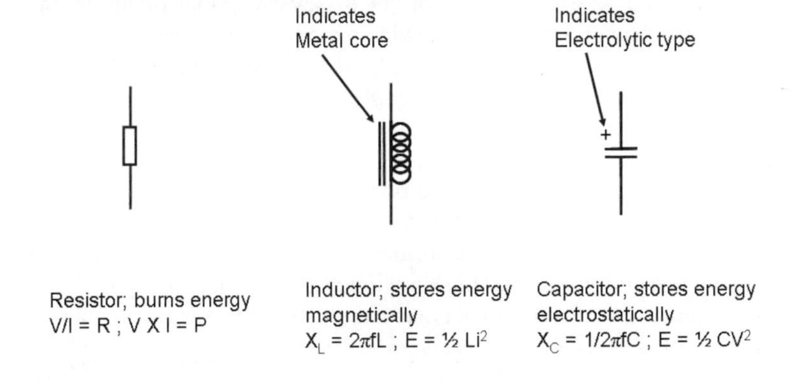

Figure 1.1 Resistors, Inductors and Capacitors

We've been talking about some quite high voltages here, because power electronics is concerned with the voltages we get from our power systems in the home and industry. For more information about these systems see box: **World Power Systems**.

World Power Systems

There are many variations on the way electricity is distributed and consumed around the world but, in general, the systems are very similar, allowing designers of most types of electrical and electronic equipment to design 'one size fits all' with some compromise. In terms of frequency, the world is divided into 50Hz and 60Hz regions, the 60Hz regions being most of North and Central America, and areas of US influence such as Taiwan, Korea etc, as well as the Middle East. Everywhere else is 50Hz, the exception being aircraft which use 400Hz. As we'll see later, the applied frequency affects the design of AC motors, but as all drives (AC and DC) rectify the mains before use, the frequency from the supply is not so relevant.

Voltage is a little more involved. Anyone using any significant amount of power such as a farm, offices or small workshop will have a three phase supply. Three phase systems are convenient for generation, distribution and consumption, and most of the world seems to find a three phase supply of about 400V pretty practical. For historical reasons, some supplies work around 380V, while others are nearer 415V or more. The US and countries closely related work with 460V or higher, but there are plenty of 60Hz supplies at 380 or 400V as well. A couple of key exceptions to this are the industrial supplies in South Africa, which has 525V nominal supply, and Canada, where the long distances make their 575V system practical. Europe is slowly rolling out a 690V supply system, but this is not widespread.

For single phase systems – i.e. domestic and light industrial systems – 230V is easily derived from 400V three phase by line to neutral connection, and similarly 220V from 380V is normal. The 460V supplies tend to transform to 200V or thereabouts, allowing a single phase supply of 115V, although the higher currents mean many appliances run a phase to phase voltage of 200V.

All these supplies are subject to variation; in countries with a good supply network, variations of less than 5% are normal. However, countries with poor supply systems, or just with long lines and variable loads may see variations of more than 10%.
So what's a power electronics designer to do?

Well, for low power applications it is possible to design drives to operate from single phase, 230V AC supplies, with enough tolerance to work down to say 200V and up to 250V or more. In practice, many of these lower voltage drives permit operation from three phase as well.

For higher voltage it's a little harder, but most designers can just about manage 380 – 500V operation, offering a special version for South Africa and Canada. We'll see later how, when rectified, 230V AC results in about 320V DC, and 400V gives about 560V, so we are talking high voltages here.

Power Factor

Once we start working with AC power, we'll talk about power factor. This can get complicated for nonsinusoidal systems, but for industrial power it can be defined as the ratio between real power and apparent power. Apparent power is the power that flows in capacitors or inductors, and is (theoretically) lossless. The current is out of phase with the voltage, lagging the voltage with an inductive load and leading with a capacitive load. In a real power system, there is always some inductance from motors, transformers etc, and these extra currents cause losses in the transmission system, so power companies prefer a high power factor, as close to 1.0 as possible (a power factor of 1.0 is a resistive load; a motor may have a power factor of 0.8, that is, some inductive load as well – see chapter 3). Some factories use banks of capacitors to correct the power factor – more of that later. Transformers and other equipment will state a kVA rating rather than a kW rating, because this accounts for the extra current due to the expected inductive load.

Mechanics

Let's keep this short. We need to know a little about the laws of motion and stuff in order to understand what the drive and the motor have to do.

Newton's Laws

Paraphrasing his laws here then (come on, you know them anyway):

1. Things stay as they are, moving or not, unless you interfere.
2. The force needed to accelerate something is proportional to its mass times the acceleration.
3. When you push something, it pushes you back with an equal and opposite force.

So:

(1) Wasn't so obvious as there was so much friction around in the old days.

(2) This is the useful one, especially when we consider rotational acceleration and torque. Remember if you are in out in space it's mass, not weight here that matters.

(3) This means if you put a gearbox on a conveyer you'd better bolt it down well, or it will shear off when the load gets up and pushes back at it.

Inertia and Moment of Inertia

We are familiar with the concept of inertia, particularly in teenagers in the mornings. That aside, (2) above states we'll need a force to accelerate a mass, or to overcome the acceleration due to gravity, otherwise known as lifting. A rotational mass, such as a wheel or motor has a rotational inertia, known as its Moment of Inertia. The symbol J is usually used for moment of inertia. If you think about it, the value is dependent on the shape of the motor or wheel. If the mass is close to the axis, the motor or wheel requires less force to accelerate it than if the mass is further out. That's why flywheels, which are designed to store energy have all the mass on the outside, and why motors designed for fast response are long and thin rather than short and fat. If you're interested in the maths, take a look elsewhere, but the square of the radius plays a big part in it. So how do we accelerate this moment of inertia? We need to look at angular motion and torque now.

Torque

Torque is the twisting force that turns things. If a linear force pushes against the outside edge of a wheel, a torque is generated in that wheel; that's what a piston in a steam or car engine does via the connecting rod. Like moment of inertia, the greater the distance it pushes from the axis, the greater the torque from the same linear force. So we express torque in terms of force x distance units, such as Newton x Metres or Foot x Pounds. If you are holding a 100kg weight with a pulley 2m diameter it is easy to see the torque needed is 981 Newton metres.
Huh? OK, the pulley radius is 1m, and the force needed to hold 100kg is 100 x 9.81 Newtons as we are struggling against a gravitational acceleration of 9.81 m/s^2. Clear now? Good. We are just holding it at the moment, not lifting it; we'll see later we need power to do that. Torque usually uses the symbol M.
This is further clarified in the diagram below.

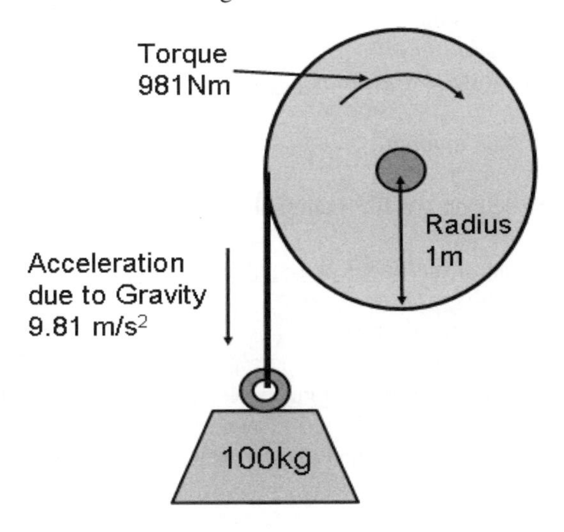

Figure 1.2 Torque

Angular motion and velocity

We're probably familiar with the idea of revolutions per minute (rpm) for engines and motors. This is a measure of rotational velocity. If we look at a single revolution we can talk about the rotational, or better, angular velocity as the angle the motor turns though in a unit of time. To make subsequent maths easier, we express this in radians per second.

A complete revolution is 2π radians (which kind of makes sense of the unit), so 60 rpm, one revolution per second, is 2π radians/second; angular velocity traditionally uses the symbol ω, which we first met in our impedance equations.

Force and Torque

So we now have two sets of laws of motion, one for linear motion and one for rotational motion. Remember the second law in particular?

Force = Mass x Acceleration

In SI units and linear acceleration, this would be:

Force in Newtons = Mass in Kilogrammes x Acceleration in Metres/sec^2

And in imperial units this is:

Force in Pounds force = Mass in pounds x Acceleration in Feet/ sec^2

Now for Rotational motion:

The equivalent second law for rotational motion is

Torque = Moment of Inertia x Rotational acceleration

In SI units:

Torque Nm = Moment of Inertia kgm^2 x Rotational Acceleration Rads/ sec^2

Where Nm is Newton.Metres and kgm^2 is kilogramme.metres^2

In Imperial units:

Force Foot.pounds force = Moment of Inertia lbft^2 x Rads/ sec^2

You can see things are so much easier in SI units, for engineers at least. So if we are accelerating a fan, we can calculate the torque needed using a rotational reading of Newton's second law. But acceleration is only part of the story. Often we are either lifting something – that is, overcoming the acceleration due to gravity, or moving against a force such as the resistance of a conveyer, the back pressure of a pump or fan, or the resistance of an extruder or mixer. Then we have to look at the work we are doing to overcome the force, and the speed at which we want to do this to give us the power required.

Although this sort of calculation can get quite complicated, we can swap between linear and rotational calculations (or guestimations), and we always come back to Newton. The conveyer system below shows how these mix together.

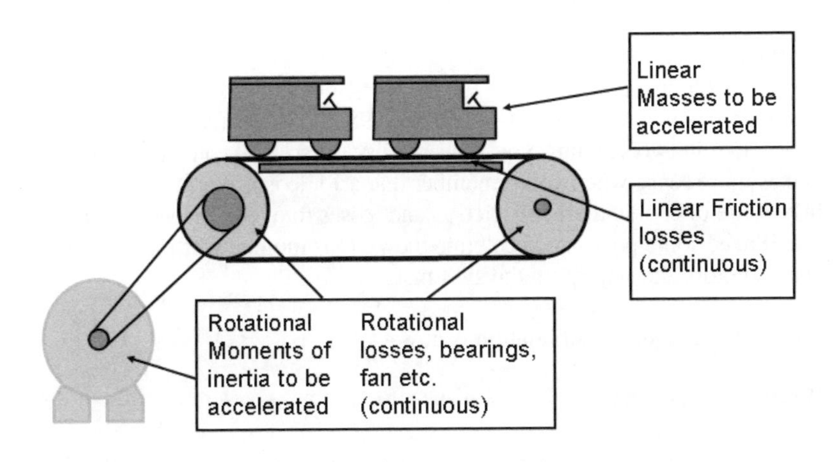

Figure 1.3 Conveyer System

Power

Power is all about doing work at a particular rate. Ignoring the philosophical interpretation of this, if you overcome a force, such as acceleration, or friction, or moment of inertia, then you do work. The quicker you overcome it, the more power you need.
In linear terms, if we are lifting something against gravity, or accelerating it, we do work, which is measured in Joules. In an engineering context, Work is the same as energy; we used Joules earlier to measure the energy in the capacitor and inductor.

Work = Force x Distance

Lift 100kg up 100m, or accelerate it at 9.81 $\underline{m/s^2}$ and you'll do
100 x 9.81 x 100 kiloJoules of work.

98100 kJ

If you do this is in one second, you'll need 98,100 Watts (say 100kW), and if you do it in two seconds, you'll need 50kW or so; you can choose. It makes more sense when you remember that a Joule is a Watt for a second. In real life of course there are friction and losses to overcome as well, and you'll need some power to accelerate the various moments of inertia of the gears, motors and pulleys in the system.

The equivalent rotational relation is now

Work = Torque x angle of rotation

So we have our pulley, which is lifting the 100kg weight, requiring 981 Nm torque, and now we want to rotate it enough to lift the weight 100m. This will need:

100/2π revolutions to do it.

But we need to use Radians for this calculation, so we must multiply by 2π. So to lift 100m we need to rotate 100 Radians.

Work = 981 x 100 Joules as before.

It sounds like a bit of a fix, but you can see that it allows engineers to work between linear and rotational calculations fairly easily. Of course, we can calculate the power as before.

Remember if you run a motor at zero speed but maximum torque in theory you need no power. Of course the current will be somewhere around the full load current in the motor (as discussed in chapter 8), and you will have enough voltage to overcome losses and to magnetise the motor, so there is significant power needed. If you increase the speed and the torque remains constant (what we engineers call a constant torque load) the power will increase linearly with the speed, because you are overcoming a force at a certain (rotational) speed.

Torque and Power

When we buy AC motors they are usually rated in kW and rotational speed in rpm. To calculate the relationship between power and torque, we'll need to convert the speed to Rads/s.

$$\text{Power} = \text{Torque} \times \text{rotational speed}$$
$$= M \times 2\pi \times n / 60$$

Where n is the rotational speed in rpm. If we want power in kW, this becomes Power (kW) = M x n/9550

This is quite a useful conversion factor when looking at motors:
37kW motor, 1450 rpm torque is about:
37 x 9550/1450 = 243Nm.

Gearboxes, belts and pulleys

Gearboxes are widely used in industry to get the right torque and speed needed. Belts and pulleys do the same thing, but tend to be limited in their ratio. As the speed is changed, the power stays the same (except for the losses of course), so the torque must rise or fall in the same ratio. I can never get the ratios the right way up, but clearly if the speed goes down and the power stays the same, then the torque goes up, so knowing the gearbox ratios, the rest follows. Exactly the same calculation is applied to belt drives, pulleys and winding systems. For belt drives, we must know the ratio of the pulley diameters to calculate their gearing. For lifting systems it can be complicated by the introduction of several pulleys or fixed ropes.

Now we use the concept of reeving ratio, where the ropes and pulleys (or block and tackle) can have the same effect as gearing. The diagram below summarises simple gearing systems.

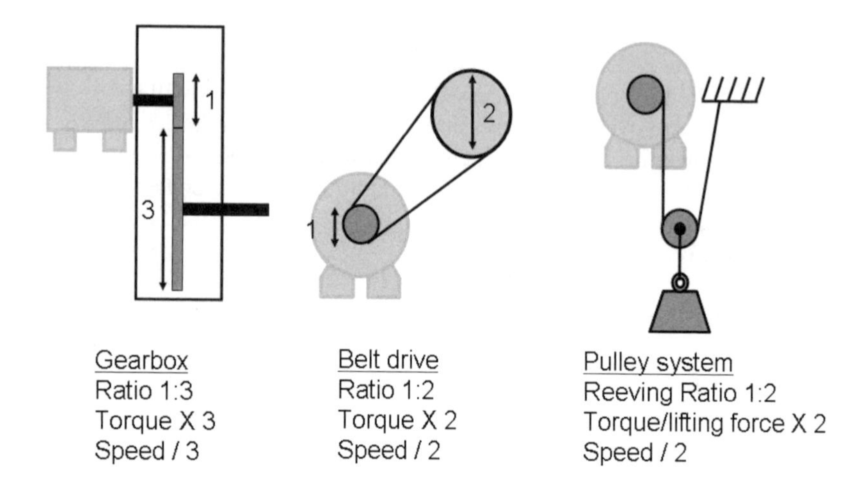

Figure 1.4 Gearboxes, Pulleys and Reeving

With these basic equations we can now calculate the amount of work needed to lift and accelerate masses in our equipment, whether they are linear or rotational. What we haven't discussed are the losses along the way and the way power is needed to move air or liquids for example. We can still use Newton's laws to some extent for the latter (see chapter 9), but losses such as friction, bearing losses, belt losses must come from experience, or at least from a detailed mechanical treatise, beyond the scope of the book.

Summary

We now have the basic laws of electricity and the passive elements in place to start looking at power electronic components, how they fit together and eventually make drives.

Mechanical stuff is all about Newton and simple linear and rotational mechanics. We must accelerate or lift, doing work and needing power, and we mustn't forget the gearing ratios and losses.

2. Power Electronic Components and Building Blocks

We've talked about the components and the basic equations that govern industrial electronics. Now let's look at some of the active components that are used in power electronics and drives. Then we'll see how they work with the passive components described in chapter 1 to handle and convert power.

Active Components

Let's not talk about semiconductor junctions and majority and minority carriers and all that. Instead, we'll look more at the practical imperfections of some of the power components used in drives. We'll see the components perform, and how their little foibles need to be understood and controlled

Diodes

Diodes conduct one way and not the other right? OK, but at high powers we need to consider the non-ideal characteristics of the diode, and consequently how different types of diodes are used in different applications.

Rectifier Diodes

These diodes sit on the AC power line and are connected in a bridge configuration to convert the AC to DC. We'll look more closely at the currents involved later, but these need to be pretty rugged devices, as they will experience surges, sags, transients etc. from the mains. For a rectifier diode on a 400V supply we'll probably select one with at least 1200V reverse voltage capability, maybe 1400V or even 1600V, depending on price. This allows for supply fluctuations, transients etc.

Now a rectifier diode isn't a perfect conductor, and has a forward voltage drop that is at least 0.5V, rising a little – but not resistively – with current. So if we supply 50A through our diode it'll lose at least 25W, so it'll need a heatsink, which can make mounting difficult (See box: **Packaging Power Electronic Components**).

As rectifier diodes are rectifying at 50Hz, switching losses (see later) are small, and 'slow' diodes can be used.

Packaging Power Electronic Components

In the bad old days the casing of the diode was at cathode (or was it anode?) potential, so a three phase bridge (see later) had four heatsinks: one big one with three diodes, and three little ones. Heatsinks were at DC or mains potential, separated by funny Bakelite spacers. The same was true of thyristors and other early power devices. Nowadays, most power semiconductors are safely packaged in an isolated pack, often called a six pack as it may contain six diodes, IGBTs or whatever. The package is a subtle design which ensures the thermal path from the chip to the heatsink is optimised, but the semiconductor is always safely insulated from the pack's base and other chips. The base is designed to be firmly attached to the heatsink, probably with the addition of a thermally conducting paste (messy stuff) to assist heat transfer. Little things, like incorporating a temperature sensor in the package, or making the connections at the same level so a printed circuit board can be easily fixed, bring benefit to the designer. The package cost is higher, but we save all the Bakelite spacers. . Different packages for diodes, IGBTs and packages with built-in drive and monitor circuits are shown in the figure below.

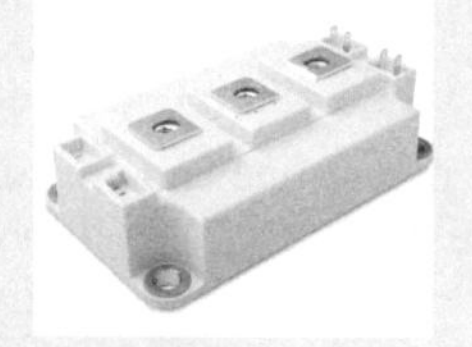

Figure 2.1 Isolated Semiconductor Packages

Flywheel or Commutation diodes

We'll see later where these important components are used in inverters and other power converters to divert inductive currents. Suffice to say that, if you are switching current on and off in an inductive load like a motor, you need to provide a path for the current to continue, or you get a very high voltage and a very big bang. This path is usually provided by a diode, known as a flywheel or commutation diode, or just com diode to its friends. The com diode has to turn off quickly when you redirect the current again – it should have a fast recovery as we say.

If you turn off – that is reverse bias any diode, there is a charge (i.e. a current for a certain time) that will flow before the diode blocks. Something to do with minority or majority carrier recombination, I think. Commutation diode action is shown in the figure below.

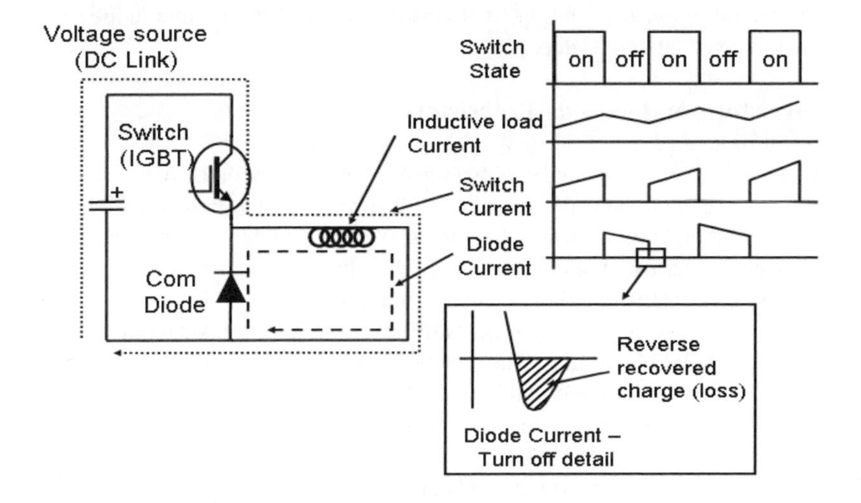

Figure 2.2 Commutation diode action

This non-ideal turn off behaviour causes losses, so the value of the charge, and the speed with which the diode blocks, determines if the diode is fast, and therefore suitable for use here. Fast diodes have a slightly lower forward voltage drop, but if we switch at high frequencies the switching losses due to the charge soon mount up, and the reverse recovered charge also makes life difficult for the other power components, because the diode looks pretty much like a short circuit while the charge is recovering. Add the fact that the reverse current can suddenly snap off, causing EMC problems, (see chapter 10) and you'll see that finding a good com diode is as important as finding good switching transistors. A typical modern fast diode can have a recovery time of 100ns, which can be a long time for a transistor looking into a short circuit.

Schottky diodes (named after Walter H. Schottky, a German physicist) have no recovered charge, but they aren't really up to power electronic voltage ratings. However, they are handy for lower power circuits. There are some promising developments with Silicon Carbide Schottky diodes but they are still a bit pricey.
Com diodes are usually mounted alongside the power transistors in the same, nice isolated package.

Thyristors, and various Transistors

- A bit of history

When power electronics was in its infancy (well childhood anyway) and dinosaurs roamed the earth, there were all sorts of contenders for the Next Power Switch. We, the design engineers, were after a neat component that was easy to control, would operate at high voltages and current, would switch quickly and would then conduct without significant losses.
Power electronic engineers are generally only interested in switching – sort of power digital electronics. The idea is that we switch our power devices on and off, we never hover half way, as this just wastes power. The better the switch, the quicker we can switch it, which, in general brings advantages, as we'll see later.
First up is the thyristor, which had been around for some time:

The Thyristor

Conventional descriptions of the thyristor talk about four layer devices or pnp/npn transistors stuck together. It's much easier to think of it as a diode which blocks current in the reverse direction as usual, but only conducts in the forward direction when a voltage pulse is applied to its gate. Trouble is, it then continues to conduct until the current in it falls to zero (natural commutation), or is forced to zero by an external circuit (forced commutation). On the other hand, if you gate the thyristor for a short time (this is usual) and for some reason the current doesn't flow. then tough, the thyristor will turn off again. We'll see later how this isn't too much of a problem if you use thyristors in place of diodes for rectification, but not much good as a power switch.
A Thyristor has an 'on' state voltage drop a bit more than a diode; maybe a volt or so. Thyristors, along with diodes, are relatively easy to manufacture at high voltage and currents, so were the first controllable components available for power electronic applications. Thyristors are still used extensively in DC drives, described in chapter 4.

If you want to use a thyristor as a proper power switch that you can turn off when you want, you generally discharge a capacitor back into it to force the current to zero. To do this you use a second thyristor. Forced commutated systems kept me amused for a couple of years during my mis-spent youth. Don't go there – my youth or forced commutation. Let's just say thyristors have the advantage they can be protected by fuses…but the fuses are expensive.

A thyristor looks like a diode with an additional low power gate connection, and was originally supplied in a non-isolated package, like the diodes described earlier. However, it was actually the first serious power semiconductor to be available in isolated packages. Revolutionary, believe me.

A triac is a bit like two back to back thyristors with a common gate connection, and can therefore control AC power with little added circuitry. For various reasons, these are best limited to light dimmers, solid state relays and similar applications
Thyristor, diode and triac symbols are shown in the diagram below.

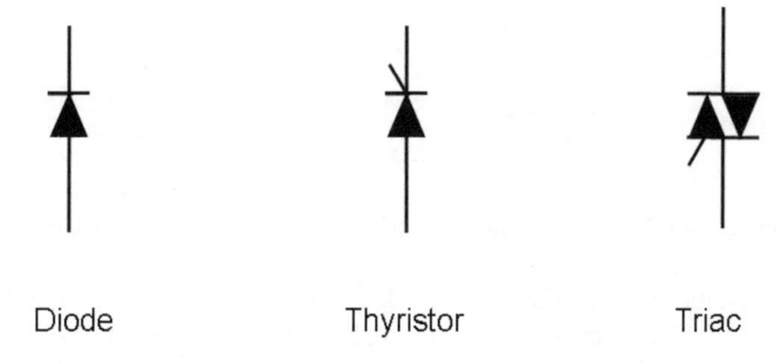

Figure 2.3 Thyristor, diode and triac symbols

- Back to power semiconductor history

We will pass rapidly over the attempts to make gate turn off thyristors (GTOs), although they actually still find application in very high power drives, say 1MW and above.

Transistors and IGBTs

In the seventies (I said it was a long time ago) semiconductor manufacturers started to be able to produce the bipolar transistor (BJT - Bipolar Junction Transistor) and similar products that would work at high voltages. Now a BJT needs quite a lot of base current to turn it on, especially when you design it for high voltage operation. You can reduce this, that is, get higher gain, by 'series' connecting BJTs to make a Darlington pair (named after a Mr Darlington of course) Shown in the figure below.

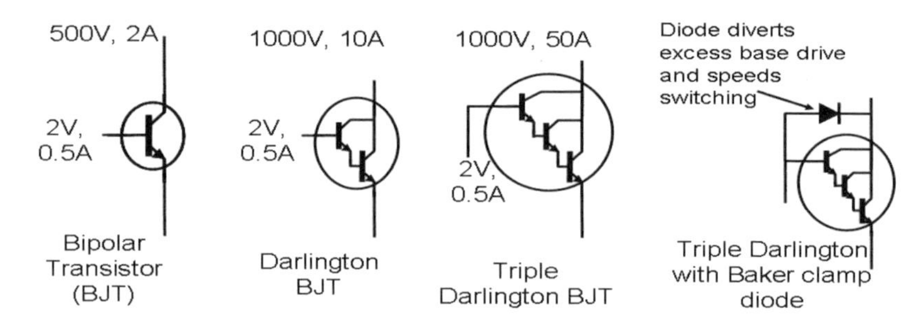

Figure 2.4 BJTs, Darlingtons, Triple Darlingtons and Baker Clamps

To get even more gain, you use three BJTs; package this with a suitably fast com diode and we're away! Well, not really; Triple Darlingtons are slow to switch off, and still need an amp or so to drive them, and with all BJTs there are restrictions on how you switch them. For example, when you turn them off you have to avoid high voltage and current - even for a short time - as this can cause instant failure, irrespective of the high power loss.

You can speed them up by fitting a diode that, when the transistor is on, diverts excess drive away from the base, speeding up the subsequent turn off as the Darlington is no longer saturated, or 'hard on' as we used to say. The diode is referred to as a Baker clamp diode, named after Mr Clamp (no, not really). You can see the whole triple Darlington thing isn't really going to work, but we all tried anyway.

Power MOSFETs

MOSFET stands for Metal Oxide Semiconductor Field Effect Transistor. You can see why we called them MOSFETs. They are field effect devices and are easy to drive with a low voltage; the gate that turns the device on and off has very high input impedance. MOSFETs also switch very fast. The catch is the 'on' state resistance, which causes quite a few losses, and rises with temperature. Higher voltage MOSFETs have a really high on state resistances, so their applications were quickly limited to single phase (230V AC – what we power engineers call low voltage) applications. Another quirk with MOSFETs is that they have built in com diodes – part of the actual structure – but these are slow, and to get round this you have to do some pretty neat (aka expensive) tricks during their manufacture, or fit blocking diodes and fast external com diodes. However, once you've sorted this you can switch pretty fast; 20 kHz is no problem in a drive application. MOSFETs are still pretty handy for switched mode power supplies (see later) and similar applications.

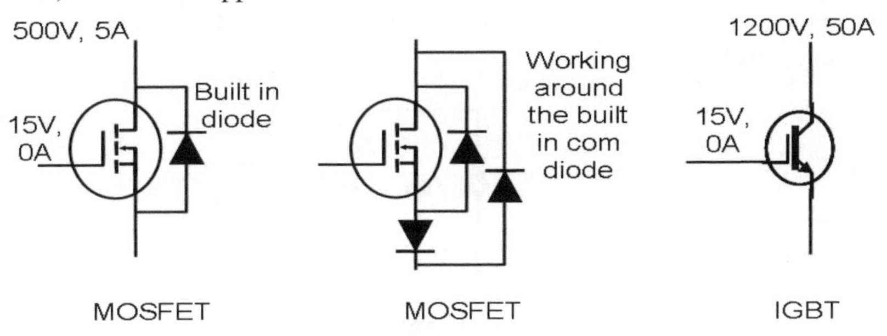

Figure 2.5 MOSFETs and IGBTs

IGBTs – Insulated Gate Bipolar Transistors

At last, the answer to our prayers! Well, again not quite, but IGBTs are now the power switch of choice for most AC drives and similar products like Uninterruptible Power Supplies. We'll look at how they perform in drives in chapter 5, but as they are voltage operated (i.e. high input impedance), like a MOSFET, they are easy to drive, and they switch pretty fast without ridiculously high losses. IGBTs are packaged up to suit their applications. They're used for switched mode power supplies in single conventional packs, but for drives they're supplied in six packs with diodes for small drives, totem pole pairs (that is, one on top of the other) with diodes for medium power, and with just a companion com diode in the largest packs. Open one of these big packs up and you'll see several IGBT and diode chips, each maybe 20mm square, connected in parallel with as many bond wires as can be packed on. These things drive locomotives. Amazing!!!
So for our drives, we'll go with IGBTs. Let's see how these get together with the other components and perform when we talk about rectifier bridges, simple converters and inverters. This will set us up nicely for DC and AC drives.

Rectifier Bridges

Rectifiers are pretty straightforward. We take the AC mains, stick it through four or six diodes in a bridge arrangement and we have DC, ready for our drive, power supply or whatever. Well not quite; starting from the beginning, let's look at a simple, single-phase and three-phase rectifier in the diagrams below.

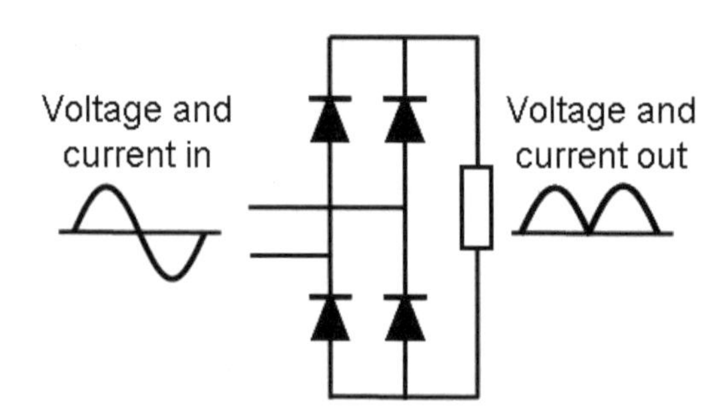

Figure 2.6 Single phase full wave bridge with resistive load

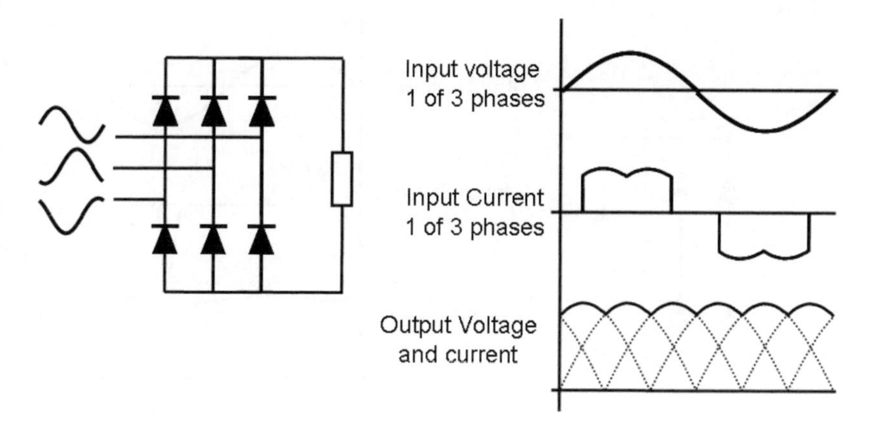

Figure 2.7 Three phase full wave bridge with resistive load

Let's initially assume a purely resistive load on the DC side. For the single-phase rectifier, the half sine waves are directed through the diodes and appear unchanged as DC, with a high ripple voltage that goes to zero every 10ms. If we use only one diode we only get one half of the waveform, but it's common to use four; this is called a full wave bridge as you get both halves of the sine wave. With all that voltage ripple it's not much use as a DC supply, but at least the current on the AC side is a nice sine wave.

However, with a three-phase bridge, the rectified half sine waves just keep coming, and the voltages overlap, with each peak contributing just 60° of conduction to the DC output, which is relatively smooth. So how does the current shape up? You can see from the diagram it is already non sinusoidal, as each phase conducts for 60° and is then suddenly commutated by the next. We'll see later how this distortion can cause problems in the supply, but worse is to come. As explained before, we may well fit a capacitor on the DC, and this changes things. The next diagrams show how the capacitor reduces the DC ripple considerably on the supply fed by single-phase mains, and makes a slight difference on the three-phase system.

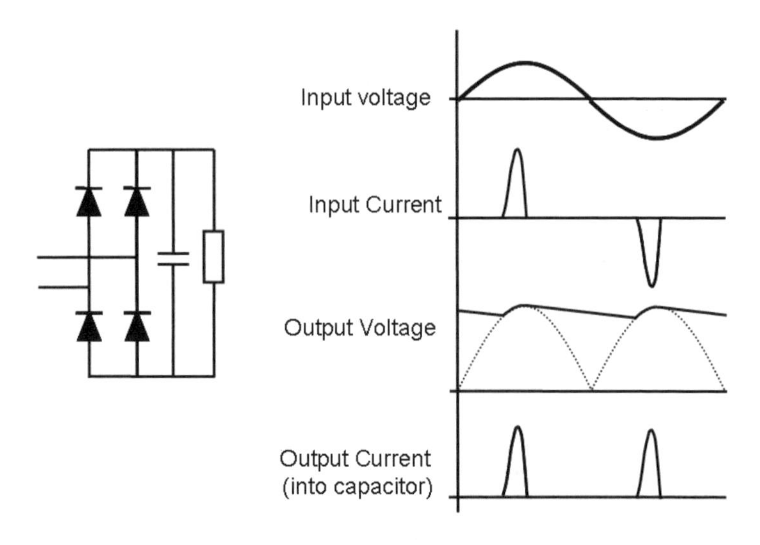

Figure 2.8 Single phase bridge with Capacitor

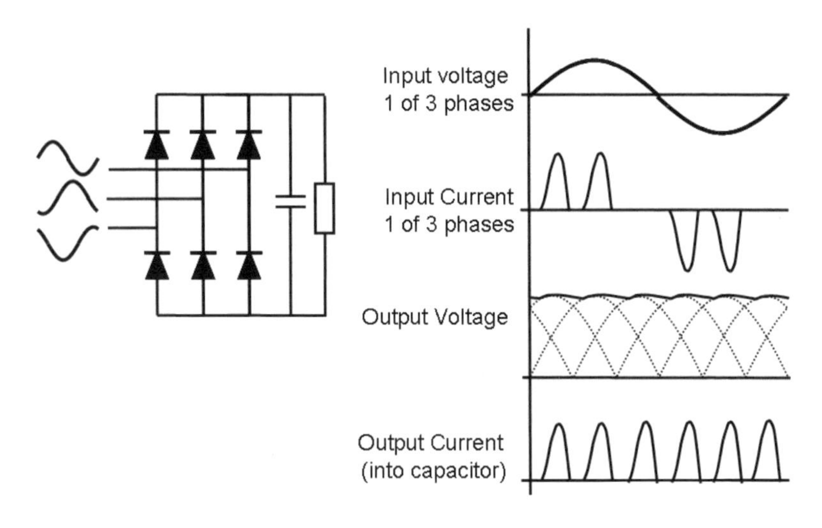

Figure 2.9 Three phase Bridge with Capacitor

The big change is in the current; in both cases the capacitor is 'topped up' in the time when the mains supply, at its peak, exceeds the capacitor voltage. If the load is light, or the capacitor very large, this is a short time, maybe 1ms. If the load is higher, the capacitor has discharged a bit more and the conduction is for longer, but then current is higher as well.

All the energy supplying the load has to flow during this short time. This means the diodes have to be pretty robust, not to mention the cabling, fusing and terminals in the system. What limits the current through the diodes and into the capacitor under these conditions? Well, nothing in the circuit, but this is real life; the current is limited mainly by the supply impedance. We define supply impedance as the percentage voltage drop in the supply at full load. A good, strong supply will have a voltage drop of one or two percent; a poor supply up to 10%. With a 'good' supply we'll get high peak currents through the diodes and into the capacitor. In extreme cases this high current will damage the rectifier or capacitors, but this isn't usual. But in any case, we are now taking nasty spiky currents from the supply, which isn't good. If the supply is poor, the supply *voltage* waveform will be distorted, which may lead to problems with other equipment (See chapter 10).

We do, however, have a pretty smooth DC supply which is close in voltage to the AC supply peak – about as high as we can get. This is now pretty useful for supplying an inverter – see later.

Back to the input currents. The shape and amplitude of the current waveform will vary a lot depending on the supply impedance, capacitor value, and load. Clearly the single phase fed capacitor needs to be much bigger if it is to keep the DC high between top ups every 10ms (8.33ms with a 60Hz supply).

How can we reduce these high currents? The usual practice is to fit an inductor into the supply; either in the DC or AC, as shown in these pictures.

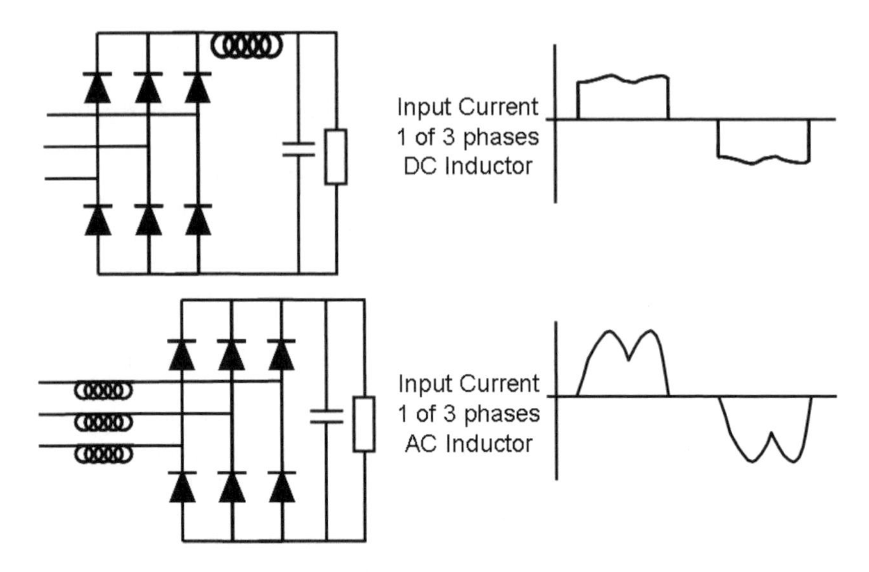

Figure 2.10 Three phase Bridges with DC and AC inductors

The jury is still out on which is the better place. On the AC side, an inductor is easy to fit externally and has no air gap; on the DC side it can be built in as standard or connected by making the terminals available, and tends to be more effective size for size. In both cases there is a reduction in the DC voltage, though less with the DC inductor. For drive applications, AC inductors are offered as "supply impedances" of say 2 or 4 percent, and may be sold as options or bought from local suppliers. DC inductors are built in or offered as optional extras by drive suppliers.

So our simple rectifier ends up with nasty currents and external components; we'll see in chapter 10 how this is just the beginning of the story of harmonics, but for now we'll just be grateful we have a high voltage DC supply available.

Stepping up and Stepping down

Or have fun with inductors, capacitors, diodes and transistors. Stepping up and stepping down doesn't directly happen within drives, except in the power supply, but it is worth explaining as it shows the sort of things that happen when you start switching capacitive and inductive loads around. Capacitors store energy as a charge, and are a handy voltage source, and inductors store energy in a magnetic field, and are a current source. We'll see that these components, together with a power switch (an IGBT for instance) and a com diode are used in nearly all switching power supplies.

Stepping voltage down

The figure below shows a simple step down converter.

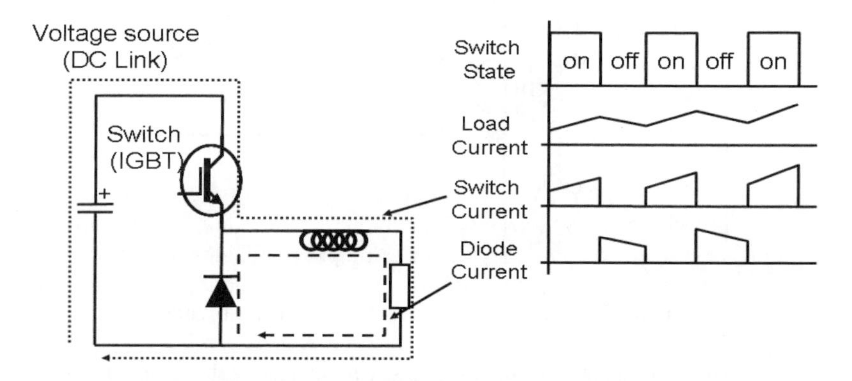

Figure 2.11 Step down Converter

We have a DC supply (i.e. a rectifier and capacitor, or maybe a battery), an electronic switch (i.e. a transistor – BJT, IGBT, MOSFET or whatever), a fast diode and an inductor. If we turn the transistor on, current will flow from the capacitor into the inductor and then into the load. If we now turn the transistor off, the current must continue to flow in the inductor, so it redirects itself around through the diode, maintaining flow in the load. If we turn the transistor on again, the diode will be reverse biased and block, and the capacitor will feed energy into the inductor again. So the inductor is 'charging' from the capacitor some of the time, and 'discharging' to the load the rest of the time.

If we switch on and off at a high frequency, the current won't vary much from cycle to cycle, depending on the size of the inductor. By controlling the on and off times of the transistor we can control the energy transfer i.e. the voltage at the load. Incidentally, varying the on off times, or pulse width in this way is known as Pulse Width Modulation or PWM for short. This simple circuit is the basis of many DC to DC converters used for power supply regulation on PC mother boards etc.
We can refine the circuit by adding a transformer, as shown in the figure below.

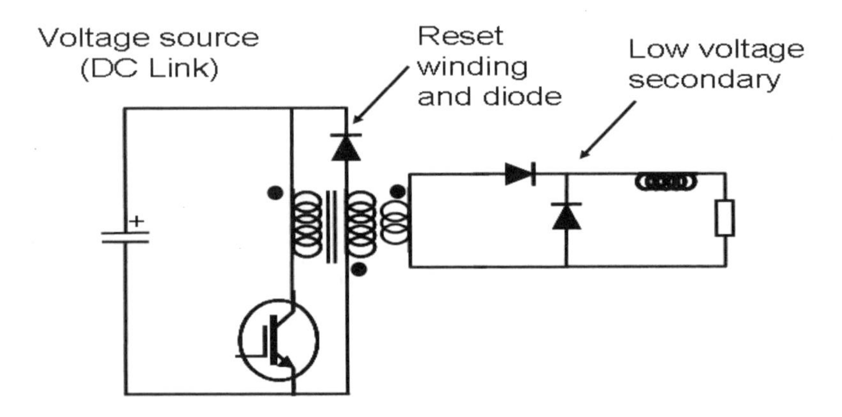

Figure 2.12 Step down Converter with Transformer

This allows the transistor to function at, say a high DC voltage, and the secondary of the circuit to supply a lower, isolated voltage. However, transformers don't like DC, so an extra winding is added that allows the transformer to reset itself when the transistor is turned off. That is, during the 'off' time a demagnetising current flows in the third winding and the flux in the transformer resets to zero ready for the next cycle.
Notice the inductor on the secondary is 'topped up' when the main transistor is 'on'. The transformer is operating at a high switching frequency, so it can be small (there is little energy storage in the short times), but it must be low loss, so a magnetic material such as a ferrite (see chapter 1) is used.
This arrangement is known as a forward converter, or buck converter, and may be used for power supplies at relatively high powers. You'll note that the secondary needs an inductor for energy storage, and if there are several secondaries this adds to the cost.

Stepping voltage up

This is shown in the figure below, and is a bit more fun.

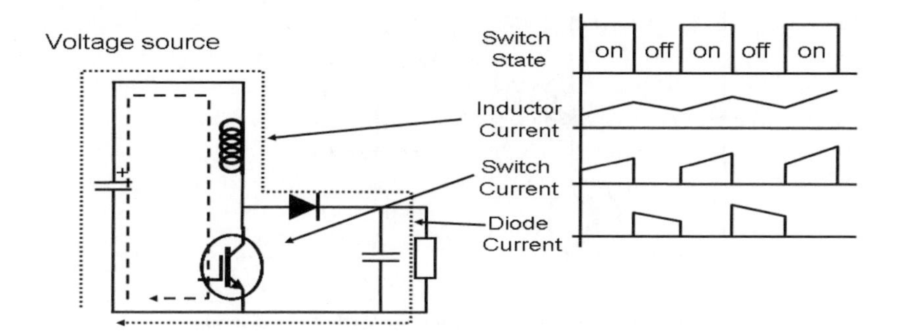

Figure 2.13 Step up Converter

We turn on the IGBT and get some current flowing in the inductor. When we turn off the IGBT the inductor current has to go somewhere, so it charges the capacitor; the voltage here can be as high as we want; the only limitation is the voltage capability of the components. Again, we can vary the pulse width to determine the energy transfer and therefore regulate the output voltage. Without a transformer, the input voltage will also be the minimum output voltage, as the supply will charge the capacitor even if the IGBT is off.

If we use a transformer, as shown below, we can get isolation as before, but if we make the 'transformer' an 'inductor' as well, we can 'charge' the primary winding and 'discharge' from the secondary windings.

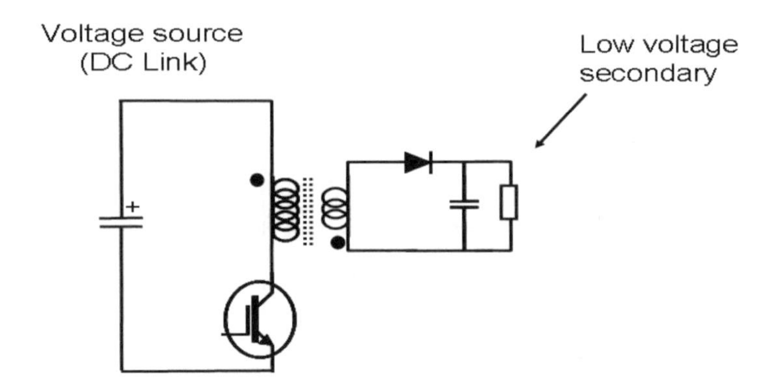

Figure 2.14 Step up Converter with Transformer

This makes transformer/inductor design a bit tricky. First of all, you'll need to add an air gap to store the magnetic energy, otherwise you just have a transformer. You'll also have to make sure the primary and secondary windings are well coupled to the core, or the energy won't transfer efficiently. If you're designing a low voltage supply, you'll also have to ensure you meet the safety clearances between the secondary and the high voltage primary. Now consider the interference radiated from the transformer, and the odd effects you get in conductors at high frequency (skin effect, inter winding capacitance etc.) and you can see it's a bit of a black art.

However, you don't need extra inductors or a reset winding like a forward converter, so this is the preferred solution for many small power supplies, including those in many drives. Because the energy is supplied from the transformer to the load 'on the fly' when the transistor is off, these designs are often called flyback converters.

There are lots of other ways of configuring diodes, transistors, inductors and capacitors to make all sorts of power converters, but it's worth understanding these simple step up or step down arrangements, because drives are all about switching inductors, emptying capacitors and commutating diodes.

Step up converters are also known as boost converters, and step down converters buck converters. With a bit of juggling you can get step up and step down, and this is known as a buck boost configuration.
Notice that in all cases we have something to store the energy, a capacitor or inductor, and that the faster we switch, the smaller the ripple current will be as we will 'top up' the energy supply more frequently. Or for the same ripple current at a higher frequency we can reduce the size of the energy storage component. Hence it is always good to switch at a high frequency, although this must be traded against switching losses in the IGBT, com diode and the passive components. In the early days of Switched Mode Power Supplies (SMPS) 20kHz was considered good, being the lowest frequency you could get away with without making audible noise. Now 100kHz or more is common, although EMC (see chapter 10) considerations can limit higher frequency operation.

Phase control

We mentioned above the thyristor, or Silicon Controller Rectifier (SCR) as our American friends like to call it. Along with diodes, thyristors ushered in the era of drives and power electronics. In fact, earlier drives had been built using Mercury arc rectifiers and thyratrons which had the advantage of glowing in the dark, but were large, expensive and lossy.
Thyristors are well suited to applications where the current naturally commutates to zero, that is, in a rectifier. If we take our standard full wave bridge and replace the diodes with thyristors, we can now choose if and when to turn on the thyristors.

If we gate them at the beginning of the half cycle, then current will flow and the thyristor will conduct, and continue to conduct (latch on) as long as current flows. We'll have the same effect as a diode rectifier bridge. However, if we delay the turn on time a few milliseconds through the half cycle, then we will only get part of the sine wave, and we'll have proportionally less voltage. By varying that delay angle (it's an angle because we are considering it as part of the half cycle of the sine wave) we can vary the thyristor bridge output voltage, as shown in the figure below.

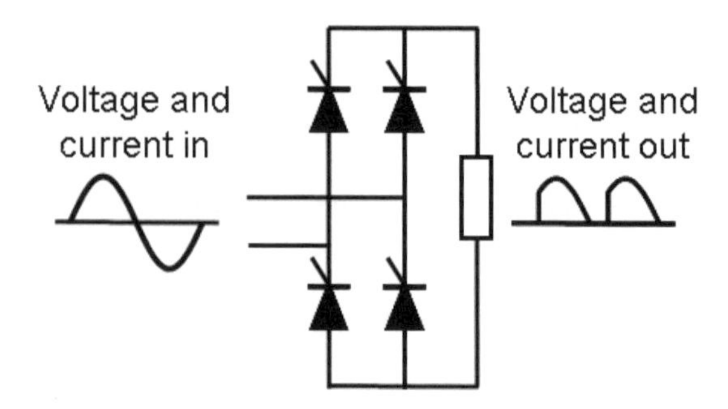

Figure 2.15 Single phase Thyristor bridge with Resistive Load

We'll see in chapter 4 how this is relatively easy to do, even without a microprocessor.
The difficulties start when we look at our various rectifier bridges and the currents in them. With a three-phase full wave bridge, if we gate the thyristor at the beginning of the half cycle, it won't conduct because another phase is still supplying the current. So no current will flow and the thyristor won't latch on. If we remove the gate drive, thinking all is well, when its turn comes to conduct, it won't and we'll have no output. The situation is worse when we add a capacitor, because we'll only conduct near the peak of the voltage –actually twin peaks depending on maximum voltages between the phases – and getting the thyristor to latch will be difficult. Engineers don't want to continuously gate the thyristors because they want to use nice cheap pulse transformers and just supply a short voltage pulse for a short time.

Of course, in the end with intelligence, experience and better thyristors and pulse transformers these problems can be overcome, but it just shows that none of these things are straightforward.
So by using phase control we can vary the output voltage of a thyristor bridge, and we can now build battery chargers, plating rectifiers, and of course, DC drives. If we use a triac, as mentioned above, we use phase control directly on AC systems and make light dimmers and disco light controllers, which made life in the 70's really exciting.

Inverters

We now come to what someone once called “A short circuit waiting to happen”. If we want to convert a DC source to a full AC source, we need a full bridge of active devices, as shown in the figure below.

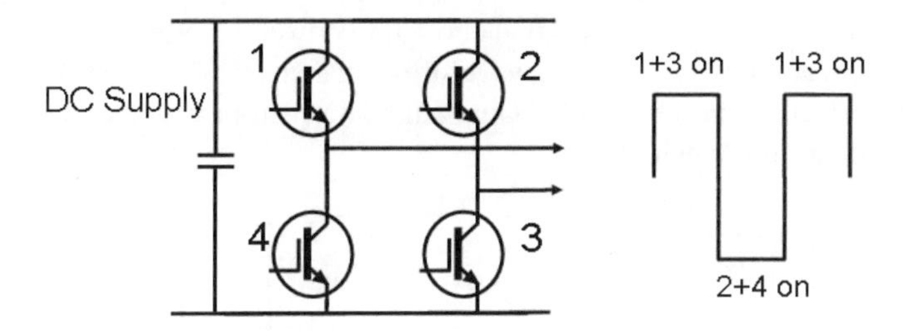

Figure 2.16 Square Wave Inverter

We now have two ‘totem poles’ as mentioned earlier, and you can see how, if we turn on transistors 1 and 3, and then 2 and 4, the load will see a positive voltage, then a negative one. The short circuit waiting to happen is turning on 1 and 4 (or 2 and 3) at the same time, or more likely, turning one of them on without allowing enough time for the other one to finish turning off. We can use a bipolar transistor, a MOSFET, or an IGBT as our switch of course, although MOSFETs and IGBTs are probably better here.

If, like with phase control, we vary the turn on time when we do this, we can control the average value of the output square wave. Of course with transistors we can vary the turn off time as well – this is pulse width modulation - PWM. This idea is shown in the figure below.

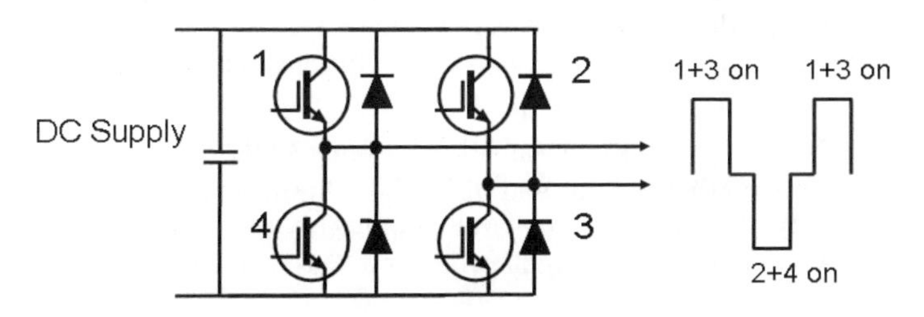

Figure 2.17 Simple Pulse Width Modulation

You'll notice we've added some com diodes now, because there are times when all the transistors are off, so we need a path for the load current if there is any inductance around – and there nearly always is. Trying to stop current in an inductor is a no no, so com diodes must be provided.
If we run the inverter from a 12 or 24V supply say, and put a suitable transformer and a bit of a filter (or combine the two) on the output, we get a pretty grotty waveform that is good enough to power a laptop (which of course immediately rectifies the waveform and steps it down again). This is how a very cheap power supply "Get mains power from your car" works, shown in the figure below.

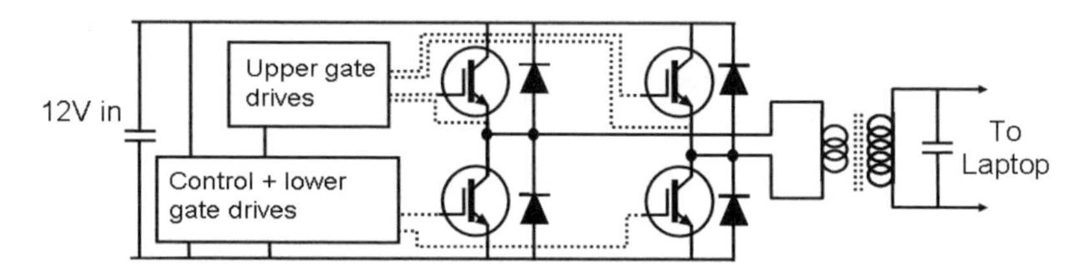

Figure 2.18 Supply for Laptop in Car

We'll see in the chapter 5 about how we develop this into a fully functional pulse width modulated variable frequency, variable voltage inverter to control AC motors, but let's just look at the problem of driving our transistors.
We have to be able to turn our transistors, IGBTs or whatever on and off easily. Driving the lower devices is no problem, as we can apply a voltage referenced to the DC negative from emitter to gate. The upper devices are different. They are referenced to a centre point that moves up and down as the transistors switch. So we really need a separate power supply tied to this point, so the gate driver can be powered, and the gate emitter voltage isn't affected by the switching action. We'll see solutions to this in chapter 7.

So inverters are a bit harder than rectifiers, phase controllers and simple converters. This explains why AC drives only really took off in the 80s as the technology of control and power electronics became available and cost effective. Also flashing disco lights were a bit passé, so engineers looked for other things to do.
Talking of control, none of this would be possible (well, cost effective at least) without the humble integrated circuit. For more about ICs, see box: **A Short History of Integrated Circuits**.

A Short history of Integrated Circuits

Early DC drives were built using individual transistors, often configured as 'long tailed pairs' for amplification, or arranged to make simple logic gates. But for serious electronics, more calculating power was needed, and the first integrated circuits, arriving in the late sixties, enabled true operational amplifiers to be used in control systems. In those days the world was analogue, and even analogue computers (using many operational amplifiers as mathematical building blocks and simulators) were built. However, logic families began to appear, and soon you could string 50 or 100 logic ICs together to build a four-function calculator (no seriously – it was offered as a kit in a hobbyist magazine).
However, the technology moved on, and soon engineers were talking about SSI (Small Scale Integration) and MSI (Medium), which included fancy pre loadable up down counters and stuff like that. At this point (say early 70's) it was possible to think about building digital drives, although nobody did. The microprocessor changed all that, and LSI (Large Scale Integration) became the buzzword. As their power developed, VLSI and VVLSI (Very, and Very Very) were actually spoken about, but clearly it was getting too silly. So from the early 80's we were able to use the power of the microprocessor and software, together with a few external chips and latches to tidy things up to produce cost effective digital controllers for everything, including drives. Finally, the ability to design your own chip (see chapter 7) allowed further reduction in component count (but a massive increase in pin count on the ICs!). However, some basic analogue components such as operational amplifiers and comparators (amplifiers with infinite gain) are still needed as buffers to the real world. We'll discuss them further in chapter 6.

Summary

We've seen that, from the early beginnings of power electronic components engineers have developed better and better power switches, including ones you can actually turn off easily. By using these with inductors and capacitors, converters can be built that use pulse width modulation to control voltage or current, stepping up or stepping down. With IGBTs, inverters can be built to power laptops in cars, if you have nothing better to do. In the next couple of chapters we'll look at motors and DC drives, and then come back to inverters when we look at AC drives.

3. Motors

Before we take a look at the drives, we need to understand the different types of motors that are used in industry, and how they work.

Basic Principles – The Electromagnetic Effect

It's pretty well known that if a conductor carrying a current is placed in a magnetic field the conductor will be subject to a force. The converse is also true; a conductor that is moved through a field will have a voltage induced, leading to current flow if there is a circuit. That's it really; that's how motors and generators work. All we have to do is come up with some way of keeping the conductor in the magnetic field, and we can motor or generate continuously. Wrapping it all up into a rotating machine seems the logical thing to do. If you want to know which way the force appears in the motor, or the current in the generator, you use Fleming's left or right hand rules – or more probably just connect it up.
Of course, the detailed design of motors and generators is highly complex, trying to minimise losses and get the magnetic fields optimised and linear, getting the excess heat out of the machine, and maintaining the insulation strength as the windings go around corners. But we'll leave that to the designers. Let's look at the simplest, oldest motor, the DC motor.

The DC Motor

All motors consist of a fixed part, usually (but not always) the outer part, and a rotating moving part. In a DC motor the rotating part carries the main current, and is called the armature. The conductors in the armature are subjected to the electromagnetically-created mechanical force that turns the motor. The field winding, which generates the magnetic field, is usually incorporated into the fixed part of the motor, the frame. Both parts of the motor include laminated steel, which provides the path for the magnetic circuit. The motor uses conventional bearings and a keyed shaft allows easy fixing of pulleys, couplings etc. This basic construction is shown in the figure below.

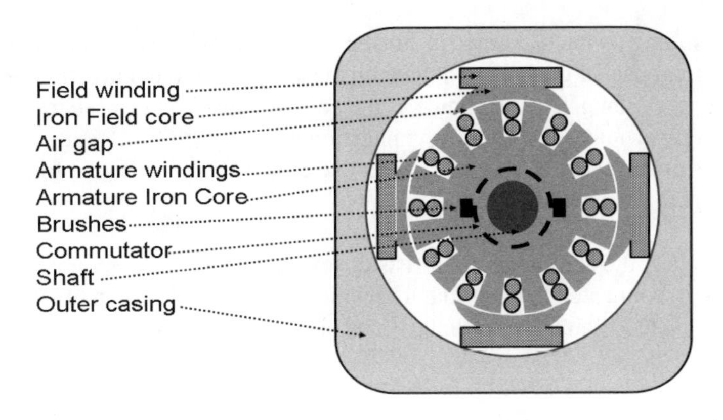

Figure 3.1 Cross Section of DC Motor

The clever part of the DC motor is the commutator. The commutator not only supplies the current to the armature, but also automatically switches it so that the current flow in each winding matches the magnetic field and the force (in a motor) is always in the same direction. This is shown in the figure below.

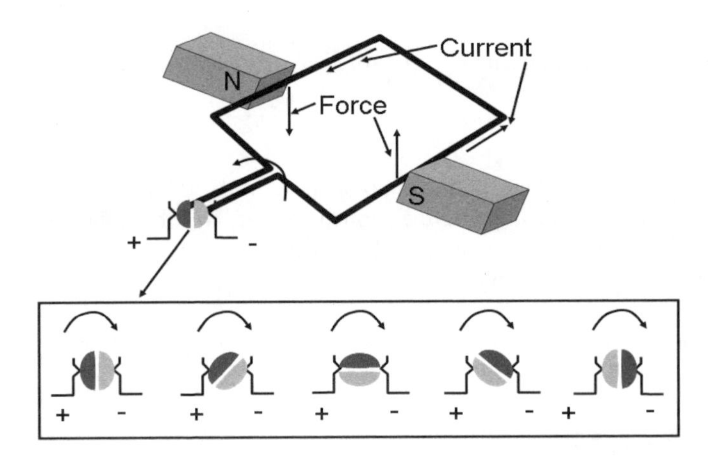

Figure 3.2 Principle of Commutation

Here, sliding contacts, known as brushes, are in continuous contact with a cylindrical pair of contacts mounted on the armature and connected to the armature winding. This is known as the commutator. You can see it cunningly switches the winding connection around just as the conductors move from one pair of magnetic poles to the opposite ones, so the force remains in the same direction.

In practice, the commutator consists of several contact faces mounted on the shaft, connected to the armature windings. The fixed carbon brushes are spring loaded against these contacts and slide easily across the contacts as the shaft rotates.

Basic Equations of the DC motor

When a motor is rotating, it is also acting as a generator, in that the rotating winding, the armature, has a voltage induced in it like a generator. This opposes the voltage that is applied to the motor, and is called the back emf (electromotive force). The back emf is proportional to the speed at which the conductor is passing through the magnetic field and the strength of the field (the flux). So our first equation is

E(back emf) = K_a(Constant) x n (motor speed) x Φ (pronounced phi - Flux)

$$\mathbf{E = K_a n \Phi} \qquad \mathbf{(1)}$$

So the back emf is proportional to motor speed, if the field is constant. Now the back emf will oppose the applied voltage, and about the only other thing to limit the applied voltage is the resistance of the armature, so the applied voltage is given by:

V(applied Voltage) = E (back EMF) + I(armature current) x R(armature resistance)

$$\mathbf{V = E + IR} \qquad \mathbf{(2)}$$

If we substitute (from equation 1) for E in this equation we get:

$$\mathbf{V = K_a n \Phi + IR} \qquad \mathbf{(3)}$$

Now the torque of the motor is produced by the interaction of the armature current and the flux; that is,
M (Torque) = K_b(another constant) x Φ(Flux) x I (armature current)

$$\mathbf{M = K_b \Phi I} \qquad \mathbf{(4)}$$

The flux, Φ, is pretty much determined by the field current.

So what do these equations tell us? Equation (3) tells us that the speed, n, is pretty well related to the applied voltage, less the armature losses. So if we increase the voltage, the speed will go up, all else being equal.
Equation (4) shows that the torque is pretty much related to the armature current, if the field remains constant. So if we want to, we can control the torque by controlling the armature current. This makes a DC motor pretty useful in tension control for example, or in an application where torque is critical at all speeds like a lift or crane. More of that later!
If we slow the motor down by adding load, the value of the back emf will fall. Equation (2) shows that, if the applied voltage remains the same, the armature current must rise to balance the loss. If the armature current goes up, we get more torque, so the increased load is quickly compensated for, with a slight drop in speed. In other words, the motor regulates pretty well, compensating for load changes in a stable way. We'll see there are ways to get improved speed regulation in Chapter 4.
What about changes in the magnetic field? Equation (3) shows that, if the flux is decreased, and if the applied voltage is constant, the speed must increase to keep the equation balanced. However, equation (4) shows that if the flux level falls, so does the torque. So deliberately reducing the field allows for increased speed, but at the cost of reduced torque. This is known as field weakening, and can be used with care. Field weakening also means that, if you lose the field supply for some reason, the motor may well overspeed if the load is low, so field loss is usually detected and the machine tripped pretty quickly.
It's pretty clear why people like the DC motor. It has natural speed regulation, simple torque control at all speeds, and separate field and armature windings that can be controlled and measured independently.
We'll see in Chapter 4 that it is relatively easy in terms of power electronics to control the armature voltage and current.

DC Motors in Practice

DC motors, of course, cannot run from the AC supply, so they are almost always used in industry with some form of speed controller. Like all machines, there are losses, which heat the motor. Because the motor's losses are largely dependent on the current, not the speed, a separately driven fan is fitted to all but the smallest motors to cool the motor. The motor will often be fitted with an encoder (on rear of motor, not shown), which is used to supply accurate speed information to the controller, and is described in chapter 8. A drive shaft of standard design and a terminal box for connection of cables are necessary of course. These features can be seen in the picture below.

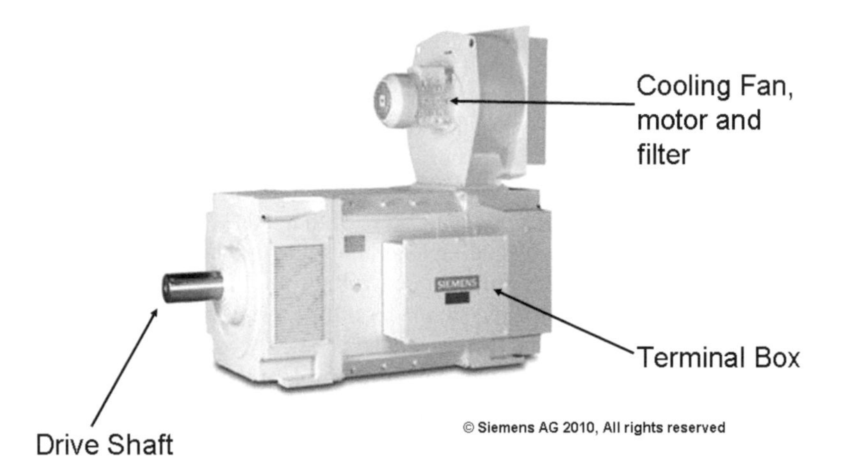

Figure 3.3 DC Motor

Most modern DC motors are of this square frame design; standard sizes allow easy exchange and installation of motors.
The motor requires little maintenance; however, brushes will wear with use, and must be periodically checked and replaced. At high armature currents and high speed, brush wear will increase, and arcing on the commutator can occur if design currents and speeds are exceeded. In this case, brush life is greatly shortened and commutator damage may take place. You can see brushes and a commutator at work on your electric drill, which is actually a series wound (see below) motor suitable for AC or DC.

Other DC Motor Designs

Normal industrial motors are configured with a separate, wound field to maintain optimum flux on the motor. These are known as shunt (i.e. parallel) motors. However, for some applications, the field is connected in series with the armature. These motors are ideal for producing very high levels of starting torque, because the high armature current also creates a high level of flux increasing further the available torque. Series motors were often used in traction applications (i.e. locomotives and light rail systems) in the past. Compound motors, that is, with field windings that are partially series and partially shunt, also have some specialist applications. These are shown in the figure below.

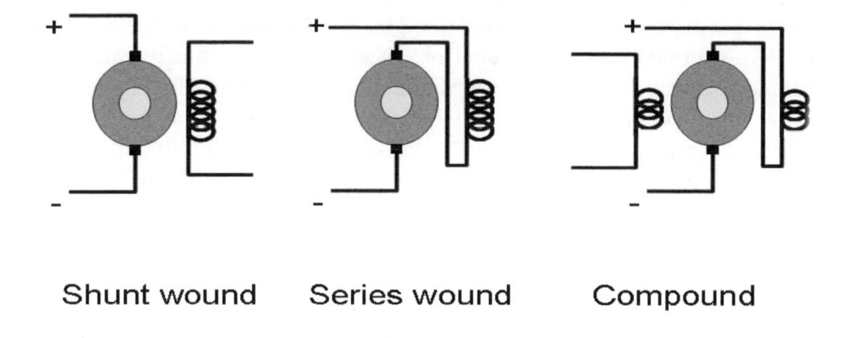

Figure 3.4 Field Connections in DC Motors

Smaller DC motors (i.e. Below 1kW) tend to be constructed with permanent magnet fields.

DC Motor Applications

DC motors are, of course, widely used in small machines, at low voltages, from computers to cars. Applications of larger DC motors in industry are generally associated with variable speed applications as mentioned above. In the past, there weren't so many variable speed applications, but most used DC motors. So you'll find DC motors and drives in older plant on equipment such as mixers, extruders and similar machines. However, DC motors and drives have been installed quite recently in applications where high torque or precision torque control is needed, or where precise speed and maybe position control is needed. Applications such as winding, paper and foil manufacturing lines, as well as high power applications in steel mills for example, continue to employ DC drives and motors. AC drives and motors are now able to meet this demand, and these are usually, but not always, now specified in place of DC.

AC Motors

Like DC motors, there are many types of AC motors and generators, but we'll look first at the most popular, the asynchronous, or induction motor.

The AC Induction Motor

Towards the end of the 19th century, Nikola Tesla developed the first practical AC motors, which, together with the use of transformers, probably tipped the balance in favour of an AC supply system. Since then, AC induction motors have become the dominant electric motor in use in industry around the world. Because of this, we'll look at them in some detail.

So how do they work? Well, let's start with a three phase transformer, shown in the figure below.

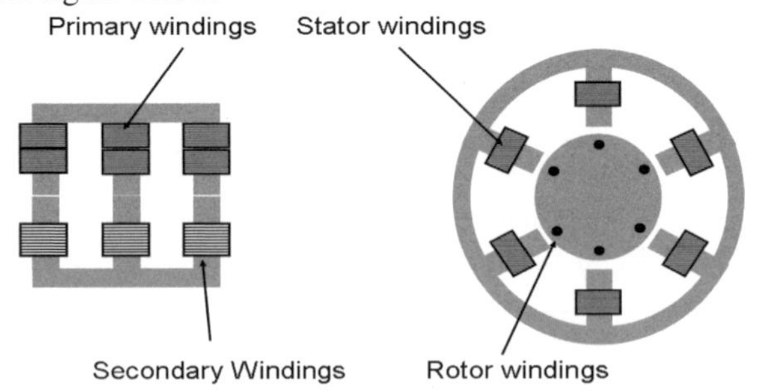

Figure 3.5 Three Phase Transformer and Induction motor

As the voltage rises and falls in the primary windings, flux rises and falls in the iron core, and voltage is induced in the secondary windings. Induction depends on the fact that the flux is changing. In a three-phase supply, the voltages rise and fall one after the other, so the voltage and frequency in the secondary is mirrored from the primary, the voltage magnitude being determined by the winding ratio.

Fine. Now let's split the primary windings and roll the whole thing up. We'll simplify the secondary by shorting the turns all together. We've drawn these windings as simple bars going into the page, and they are shorted together at each end of the rotor. We'll put an air gap between the primary and secondary parts of the iron so the middle bit can move. Let's call the middle bit the rotor, and mount it on bearings. We still have transformer action, but we have a magnetic field, and some conductors in the rotor carrying current. With a field and a current we get a force on the rotor windings, so they start to move. Remember the DC motor with its field winding that builds a magnetic field, so any armature current generates a torque? Well, we have the same sort of thing here.

So far so good? Now for the tricky bit. The primary winding – let's call it the stator – is connected to a three phase supply, so the voltage in each winding is AC, and so the resultant magnetic field is also alternating. Luckily, phase voltages follow one another in a logical way, so the magnetic field appears to move from one winding to the next. That is, in our round transformer, the field rotates, providing you've connected the stator windings correctly.

As each rotor conductor – carrying induced current - is subjected to this field, the force gets it moving and pretty soon the whole rotor is catching up with this rotating field. If it catches up, that is, if it is *synchronised* with the rotating field, it won't see any more changes in flux, so there won't be any transformer action any more, so there won't be any rotor current induced, and no force; that is, torque. So the rotor will always run a little slower than this rotating field, or there won't be any torque to keep it moving. This lag, or difference in speed, means that there is a frequency difference of a few Hertz between the rotating magnetic field and the rotor speed, so transformer action can take place.

How fast is it going? Well, this depends on the number and arrangement of the windings, and on the supply frequency. A motor with the minimum number of windings or poles (two) will rotate at close to the supply frequency of 50Hz; that is just below 3000 rpm (or 3600rpm on a 60Hz supply). Different winding arrangements such as a four-pole motor give an operating speed close to 1500 rpm (1800rpm on 60Hz). But remember, to generate any torque the motor always needs to run a bit slower, so that's why it's also called an asynchronous motor. If the motor is loaded, it will slow down, the difference frequency will increase, and more current will be induced in the rotor, increasing the torque and taking up the load. The reduction in speed from synchronism, always necessary in an asynchronous motor, is called the *slip*.
So we have a motor that runs close to, but not at, its synchronous speed, and that, when loaded, slows a little but not a lot. Typical slip on a small motor will be about 10% at full load, and on a large motor only 2 or 3 %; so the natural regulation of an induction motor is pretty good. It's pretty easy to make and buy motors with 2, 4, 6 or 8 poles, giving speeds as shown in the table below. Remember synchronous speed is never quite achieved and even with nothing connected to the motor there will be losses due to the cooling fan (stuck on the end of the shaft) and friction.

Number of Poles	50Hz Synchronous Speed	50Hz Full Load Speed	60Hz Synchronous Speed	60Hz Full Load Speed
2	3000	2850	3600	3450
4	1500	1350	1800	1650
6	1000	900	1200	1100
8	750	700	840	790

Most industrial motors have four poles as this is a convenient speed. Six and eight pole motors are often a little larger than standard to accommodate the extra windings.

Clearly the induction motor has a lot going for it. No brushes or commutator, direct connection to the supply and speed regulation good enough for most applications. As most rotors are stacks of laminated steel with the conductors cast in (using aluminium or, more recently, copper) they are cheap to manufacture, with only the stator winding to prepare and press into the frame and laminations. Because of the arrangement of the rotor winding (a series of vertical bars joined at the top or bottom), induction motors like this are sometimes called squirrel cage motors, although not having seen a squirrel cage I cannot vouch for the similarity or otherwise. Hamster wheel motors, by comparison, doesn't seem so catchy a phrase somehow.

There are hundreds of millions of induction motors in use around the world. Let's look a little more closely at this unassuming machine.

Induction Motor Theory and Operation

The equivalent circuit of an induction motor is shown in the figure below.

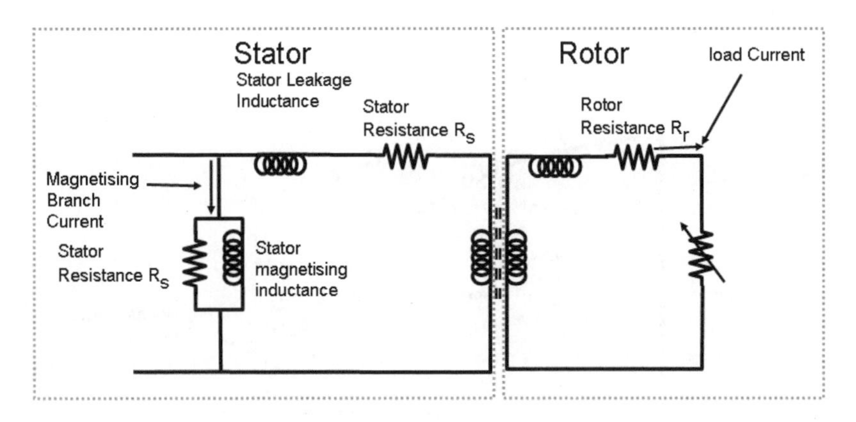

Figure 3.6 Induction Motor Equivalent Circuit

The circuit, with variations, is widely used for analysis and simulation of a motor. Essentially, we have an ideal transformer linking the stator and the rotor. However, because our real motor/transformer has an air gap and lots of iron, there is a significant magnetising current that flows, irrespective of load current. This is shown flowing in the magnetising branch of the stator, through the stator inductance and sets the flux level in the motor. The current to the rotor and load also flows in the stator, this current reaches the rotor via the transformer.

This goes through the stator resistance (which is also part of the magnetising branch) some stray inductance in the stator, and then through the transformer to the rotor, which also has some inductance and resistance. The energy of the load now appears as a resistance in the rotor, which varies dependent on the slip, s. Actually, the effective load resistance can be shown to be:

"Load resistance" = Rotor resistance (1-s)/s

This means for small values of slip, the load resistance is high, but as the slip increases the load resistance falls, therefore drawing more current and generating torque as explained earlier.
We can use the equivalent circuit to analyse more closely what happens with loading and starting, but the mathematics gets a bit complicated. What we end up with is a graph, shown in the figure below, which is familiar to motor and drives engineers alike.

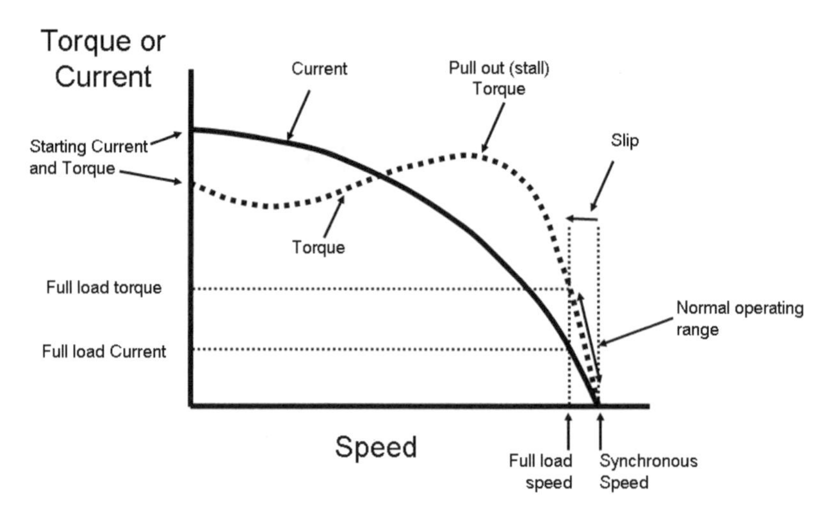

Figure 3.7 Torque Speed diagram of an Induction Motor

What does the graph show? Firstly, we can see the normal operating range is at a speed close to the synchronous speed. As the load changes on the motor, the speed varies slightly (the slip), depending on the slope of the graph at that point. Remember, the synchronous speed is dependent on the motor design (number of poles) and the supply frequency, so in practice our four pole motor may be running at 1490rpm (1790rpm with 60Hz supply) with no load, and 1380rpm (1680rpm at 60Hz) at full load.
As the load changes, the current will increase accordingly to take up the torque. The normal maximum operating point – in terms of current or slip - is determined by the motor losses and the design of the flux in the motor, but is way below the maximum, or pull out torque. If the load does exceed this maximum, the motor will stall, and come to a stop, drawing a correspondingly high current. This is known as locked rotor condition.

The same conditions occur at start up. The high 'locked rotor' current and torque will get the motor going, and the motor will accelerate to the normal operating point quite quickly. However, these starting currents are typically six times full load current, so motors must not be subjected to too many starts in a short time, or they will overheat. If the load has a high inertia, like a fan, the acceleration time can be quite long, also causing prolonged high currents and leading to the motor overheating anyway. We'll see later that variable speed drives get round this.
Another solution to limit starting current is to reconnect the motor windings in a star configuration, switching over to a delta configuration after a short time. Star/Delta starting is common with motors above say 30kW, and is described below. For higher powers, transformers can be used, or even thyristor controllers – soft starters - but this is getting messy…

Reversing

It's quite common to need to reverse an induction motor. Actually this is pretty easy. We have a rotating magnetic field due to the phase sequence of the three-phase supply on the motor. Swapping any two phases will reverse the direction of rotation of this field, and therefore the motor. You can imagine the effect of doing this while the motor is running; so reversing contactors are carefully sequenced. We'll see later that reversing a motor is pretty straightforward when using a drive, another argument for the drive salesman.

Magnetising Current and Power Factor

The equivalent circuit shows us that, even with no load, there is a magnetising current flowing in the stator. One of the confusing things about induction motors is that the magnetising current and the load current are all mixed up as the stator current, unlike in a DC motor, where they are separate as field and armature currents. So if we run the motor at no load, the magnetising current will be pretty much all we see. This can be 20% of the full load current, but with a very poor power factor. That is, there is a lot of current flowing around the motor, but not doing any work. Even when the motor is loaded, the power factor may only be 0.8 on a typical motor. In either case, this results in a typical factory having a power factor that is nowhere near 1.0, and power companies really don't like this, because that current has to flow around their transmission system causing losses, but not being paid for. However, this is the nature of induction motors, and although designs are being improved to increase efficiency as well as power factor, traditional solutions such as power factor correction systems (basically banks of capacitors on the supply) are still needed in many plants.

Flux and Voltage

So there is a magnetising current that is setting the flux level in the motor, and of course we need this flux in order to produce torque. The magnetising current will be set by stator inductance, the applied voltage and the applied frequency, according to the equation for current flow in an inductor, from chapter 1.

$V = 2\pi fL \times I$.

Rearranging:

$I = V/2\pi fL$

The current sets the flux, so as the stator inductance (L here) is constant, increasing the voltage increases the flux, while decreasing the frequency increases the flux. Put another way, if you decrease the frequency, you'd better decrease the voltage to keep the flux constant. These relationships become important when we start trying to control the speed of the motor in chapter 5.

Generating

If, for some reason the motor is driven above synchronous speed it will start to drive energy back into the supply. This is a little difficult to imagine, firstly because the supply needs to be present to supply magnetising current, and secondly because the energy reversal takes place by phase change of the current, rather than the current being positive or negative, like in a DC motor. The figure below shows the magnetising currents and load currents for one phase of motor when motoring with full load, no load, and then generating.

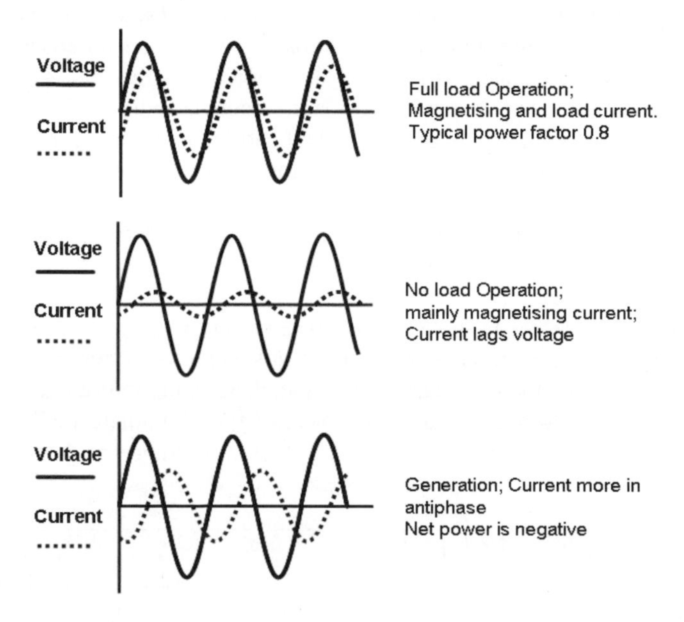

Figure 3.8 Induction motor currents On and Off load; Generating

Generation, or regeneration, doesn't occur very often with induction motors connected to the mains, but we'll see it's important when motors are used with variable speed drives.

Induction motors in Practice

Induction motors are manufactured in very large quantities in power ratings from a few Watts to many Megawatts. Standard designs are available from typically 60W to 1000kW with 2, 4, 6, or 8 poles to suit most industrial three phase supplies. The electrical and mechanical construction has been standardised and many mounting options are available.

Standard Motors - NEMA or IEC?

As is often the case, the world is divided between US and European Standards. In practice, US standard motors, known as NEMA (National Electrical Manufacturers Association) motors are used in countries with 60Hz supplies (see chapter 1). They are also dominant world-wide in the oil and gas industry, and of course will appear in machines built in NEMA countries that are then exported to around the world. Naturally these motors are designed primarily for 60Hz supply operation, and are rated in Horsepower.
IEC (International Electrotechnical Commission) standard motors are optimised for 50Hz supplies, and are found in most of Europe, Asia and Africa. They are rated in kilowatts.
IEC motors will generally show 50 and 60Hz ratings, and standard power ratings for motors are the same, but in kilowatts and horsepower. For example, a 7.5kW motor will carry 50Hz and 60Hz rating information, where the 60Hz information states the power as 10Hp. As there are 746W in a horsepower, the numbers fit. Some standard power ratings are shown in the table below.

5.5kW	7.5kW	11kW	15kW	18.5kW	22kW	30kW	37kW	45kW	56kW	75kW
7.5Hp	10Hp	15Hp	20Hp	25Hp	30Hp	40Hp	50Hp	60Hp	75Hp	100H

Remember, these power ratings are the mechanical power at the shaft. The electrical power will be greater than this due to losses, and the kVA input will be even higher, due to the lagging power factor. See later and Chapter 7, for more about efficiency.
We'll look mainly now at IEC motors, although NEMA motors are generally similar. Actually NEMA sizes are generally larger than IEC motors, which mean they have more copper and steel in them and are therefore often more efficient, although IEC motors are catching up.

Motor Frame Sizes

Motors are mechanical, so motors are listed by mechanical output power or frame size. The Frame size (FS) of an IEC motor is the based on the height of the shaft above the mounting datum in mm, and always seems rather small! For example, our 7.5kW four pole motor is built in FS 132 M, at least by one major manufacturer. This means the centre of the shaft is 132mm above the mounting level. The M refers to the length of the motor; S, M and L allowing for Short, Medium and Long motor lengths. The key dimensions of an IEC motor are (or should be) identical, so motors from different manufacturers are interchangeable. These dimensions, motor performance (especially efficiency), mounting methods etc. are all defined in several IEC and EN standards.

Mountings

We think of the standard induction motor with standard foot mounting, but there are many different mounting possibilities that are defined and standardised. Some of these are shown in the figure below.

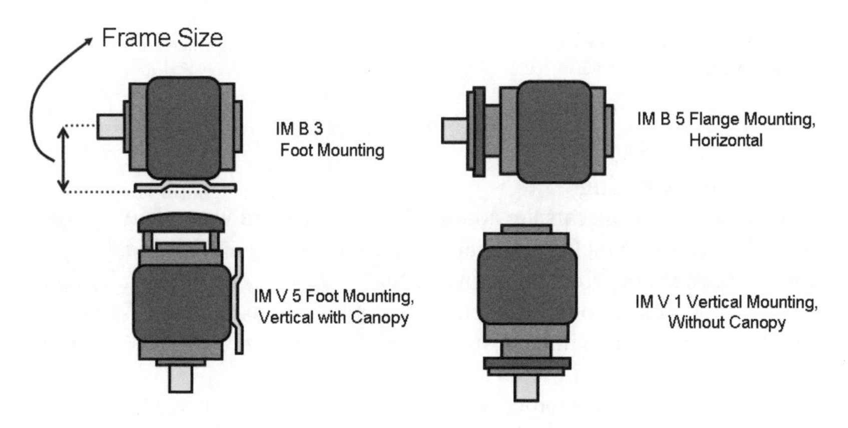

Figure 3.9 Some Typical Motor Mountings

Motor Rating Plate

If you want to know about the motor in your factory, look at the rating plate. It will tell you nearly everything you need to know. A typical rating plate is shown in the figure below.

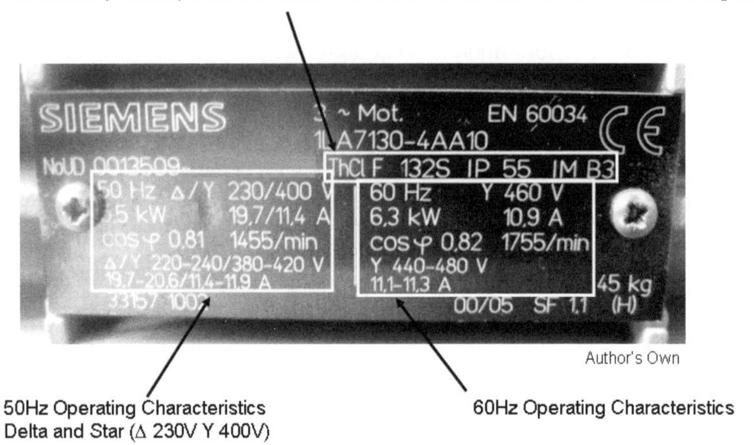

Figure 3.10 Motor rating plate

Options and Cooling

Although induction motors are constructed in a standard way, many options are available. These include special or different bearings, mechanical brakes, encoders, different operating voltages etc. This can make ordering a standard motor quite complicated if these options are requested. Of course, many users of motors will have special requirements, and will have custom motors designed and built to meet these.

Unlike DC motors, AC motors are designed primarily to run at a fixed speed, connected directly to the three phase supply. Therefore a fan can be mounted as directly on the shaft to provide cooling, running at the same speed as the motor. The fan directs air over the outer casing of the motor, which is usually ribbed to help cooling. This cooling is adequate in many cases when the motor is operated at variable speed, providing the motor doesn't run at a low speed, and a high current for too long. If this is anticipated, the motor can be specified with a separately driven fan; in practice this is unusual.

The figure below shows many of the features common to AC motors.

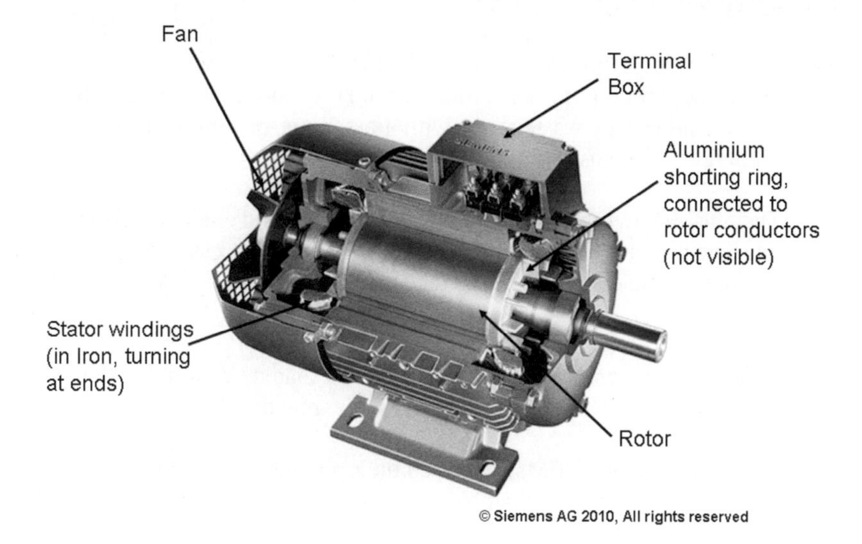

Figure 3.11 AC Induction motor with Cutaway

This is a typical motor of several kW, with conventional aluminium cast rotor conductors, buried in the rotor with only the end shorting connections visible. Some new motors have copper rotor conductors to improve efficiency. Actually improving efficiency is a fairly hot topic (see box: **Rules, Regulations and Efficiency**), but motors have been around a while, and it's difficult to make them a lot better without extra cost (like copper rotors).

Rules, Regulations and Efficiency

There are a lot of motors around, and for some time now governments have been interested in improving the efficiency of new motors, with a view to reducing overall energy wastage. As with most things governments do, there are a few problems:

1. There are an awful lot of motors already in use, and even though an inefficient motor costs a lot more in energy than the cost of upgrading to a more efficient motor, users take the "If it ain't broke, don't fix it" view.

2. Similarly, rewound motors are less efficient than new ones, but the old habit of getting motors rewound all the time dies hard.

3. Machine builders (OEMs), who sell their products on to other users, have no interest in fitting a high efficiency motor; they usually just want the cheapest.

Of course, motor manufacturers want to sell motors and save the planet at the same time, so they have been improving efficiency and preparing free software programmes that show the payback time of changing out motors, or even better, fitting a drive and motor. Regulations (that is, Euronorms in Europe and EPact - the energy policy act - in USA) have driven new standards in efficiency, so that the old standards in Europe, EFF2 and EFF1 have been superseded. In any case, going more efficient would mean EFF0, so a new standard calls for IE1, IE2 and IE3, where IE3 is the most efficient, These standards are being phased in over the next few years, but interestingly (are standards ever interesting?) by 2017 motors must either be IE3, the highest category of efficiency (and quite hard to meet), or they may be IE2 and used with a drive. (IEC 60034-30). Of course, this has big implications for the motor business, and maybe more for the drives business.

Supply Voltage and Star Delta Starting

We mentioned earlier that the starting current on induction motors can be six (or more) times the full load current, and the motor may be configured for star delta starting. Let's look at this in more detail.
For very little extra cost, both ends of the three windings of an induction motor can be brought to the terminal box; and they normally are.
This allows the motor to be configured in a star or delta connection. Small IEC motors tend to be designed for 230V operation when connected in delta, and 400V operation in star. However, larger industrial motors are rated at 400V in delta and 690V in star. This means if they are started at on a 400V supply in star connection, the starting current (and torque) will be greatly reduced. In many applications this is an advantage, and the star/delta starter can be set up to switch over when the motor is close to operating speed. Three contactors, a timer and careful wiring are required for star/delta starting. Star and delta connections and switching are shown in the figure below.
With or without star/delta starting, too many starts can overheat a motor as well as stressing the insulation; a good argument for fitting a drive, as we'll see later.

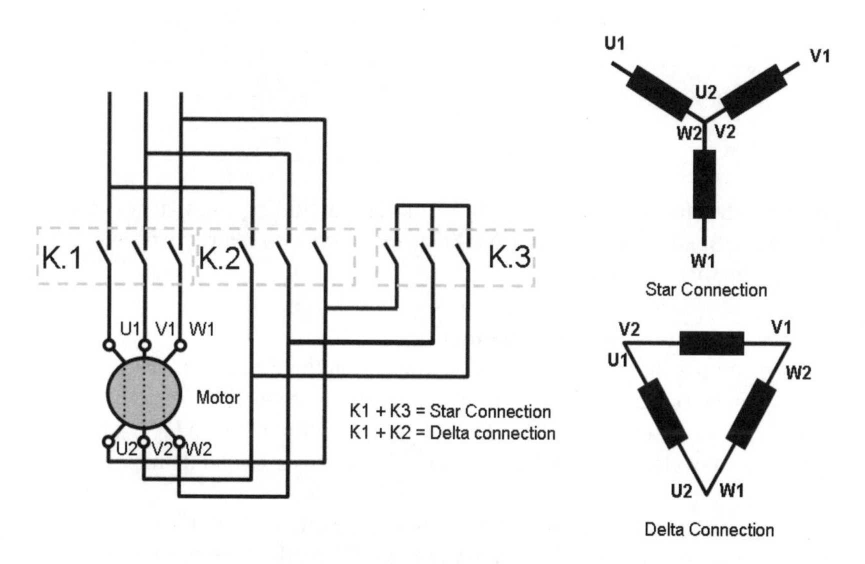

Figure 3.12 Star Delta Starting

Duty Cycles and Insulation Ratings

Induction motors have a high thermal mass, so they can be utilised in overload for a short time, depending on the nature of the overload. IEC motors are specified for certain overloads. These are defined from S1 (continuous operation at 100% load) to S9 (continuous operation with speed and load changes). Careful analysis of loading and use of these ratings allow a motor to be reliably specified for overload operation.
If a motor gets too hot, the insulation on the windings will fail. The insulation is specified according to internationally recognised standards, valid for NEMA and IEC motors. These classifications are shown in the table below. Many motors are designed for Class F temperature, but use Class H insulation. That is, the maximum (worst case) temperature for the winding in the motor is 155 °C, but the insulation is rated at 180 °C, giving a safety margin. Insulation tends to deteriorate with time, especially at high temperatures, leading to stator winding failure. The stator windings can be rewound and repaired, but this affects the efficiency of the motor, as mentioned earlier. Sensors may be embedded in the stator windings to monitor temperature.

Insulation Class	Temperature °C	Temperature °F
A	105	221
B	130	266
F	155	311
H	180	356

Incidentally, most of the standards for motors, including sizes, duty cycles etc. are defined for Europe in EN60034, which runs to many parts, and is a fascinating bedtime read.

Motor Construction and Protection

Motors are out there in the factory, or outside in the weather. Consequently, they must be protected from dirt, dust and liquids, as well as frost and direct sun. A motor sitting under a coal conveyer will soon collect a layer of coal dust that may affect the cooling, or get into the bearings and damage the motor.
Motors must also be pretty strong. They will be climbed on, hit by forklift trucks, shaken, stirred and generally abused. Particular care must be taken with the connections, as contamination can enter via the same route as the cable, and the terminal box cover must make a good seal and must be easy to use.

As a result of these requirements, motors are painted with a good quality paint, and essentially sealed to prevent anything getting onto the windings or terminals. The protection level is usually IP55. We'll come across these ratings later, so the Box explains them briefly.

Protection Levels

A well recognised standard is EN60529, which defines protection levels of equipment such as electrical cubicles, products like drives as well as motors. The definitions of the protection levels are pretty well described in the standard, but a rough and ready explanation follows (don't quote me!). The protection level of a product is generally expressed as IPXY, where X defines the protection from dust and dirt, and Y the protection against fluids. The bigger the number the higher the protection. The table below gives approximate descriptions for each number.

Number	Meaning of first digit (objects) X Protection from...	Meaning of second digit (fluids)Y
0	No protection	No protection
1	large bodies 50mm diameter	Dripping water from vertical
2	Fingers, 12mm diameter	Dripping water from vertical +/- 15°
3	Tools, wire etc 1mm diameter	Sprayed water from above +/- 60°
4	Objects 1mm diameter	Splashes from all over
5	Dust causing damage	Water jets all over
6	Any dust	Heavy seas
7	-	Immersion
8	-	Complete, continuous immersion

Needless to say, not all combinations of numbers are common, and certain combinations come up time and again:

IP00 This is an open chassis with no protection, probably for building into equipment with its own casing.

IP20 This is finger protected, and is typical of equipment containing high voltage, but is installed in a cubicle.

IP21 as IP20, but with a bit of a roof to stop dripping water or dirt falling inside.

IP42 This is just about passable as suitable for mounting on a factory wall.

IP54, IP55, IP56 These are the protection levels usually expected for cubicles or other equipment installed in industrial plant, and is just about OK for fitting outside.

For 'on deck ' marine applications you'll need IP67 at least, but in any case there are separate standards for ships.

Increased Safety
There are special rules for operating motors in inflammable or explosive atmospheres, and motors must be designed to contain any explosion or arcing that occurs inside them. The motors, built according to these ATEX (in Europe) regulations, are usually more expensive and larger than standard motors.

Induction Motors for Use with Drives
Design of AC motors has always focused on the standard mains connected motor, and at least 90% of the world's motors are used this way. The design is compromised to some extent to allow for easy starting, supply variations etc. More recently, induction motors have been designed specifically for use with drives, which has led to performance improvements in terms of higher torque and better regulation. These motors are often built with encoders (see chapter 8) to enable position and speed control, and are therefore used in applications such as printing machines, foil winders and machine tools. Needless to say, these motors and drives are expensive and intended for high performance applications, which we aren't really going into in this book.

Synchronous Motors
We've looked in detail at the asynchronous motor, but what happens if we replace the rotor in an induction motor with an assembly of electromagnets or permanent magnets? Well, put simply, the rotor will be forced around as before, but there will be no slip, so the motor will run at synchronous speed. Hence the name. Synchronous motors are therefore very useful if you need a precise speed like a clock drive – you can usually count on the supply frequency to remain pretty stable. However, in industrial applications this isn't very often needed, and in any case these days you would probably go for a motor and drive combination to achieve the desired effect, so synchronous motors are pretty unusual, and their cost reflects this. With no natural regulation (if the load rises the motor speed remains the same until it stalls) and difficult starting they are not popular.
If the rotor is a wound rotor, the connections can be brought out on slip rings, and the rotor field strength controlled. This is particularly useful if the machine is a generator, and this is how most electricity is generated, but that's another story.

Synchronous motors with permanent magnet rotors have no rotor losses and are therefore more efficient than asynchronous motors. As they can be used with drives, there is renewed interest in this technology, particularly with powers below a few kilowatts.

High Performance and Specialist Motors

The combination of a permanent magnet rotor and a fixed stator winding leads to many exotic possibilities with motors. In particular, a DC motor can be turned inside out so that the armature is on the outside and the field (now consisting of permanent magnets) on the inside. Some feedback from the rotor tells the drive (they only work with drives) how and when to power the windings. There are no brushes or commutator, so these motors are called (imaginatively) brushless DC motors. They are particularly useful for high performance and positioning applications, so again are a bit beyond the scope of the book.

Summary

Although DC motors have commutators and separate windings for field and armature, they are easy to control and have proved ideal for many applications. AC induction motors are much simpler and cheaper to manufacture; their speed is largely dependent on the applied frequency and winding configuration.

4. DC Drives

Introduction

In Chapter 3 we saw that a standard industrial DC motor (or generator) usually consists of a rotating armature and a fixed field winding in a robust steel casing. The armature is supplied through a commutator and brushes, which, as the armature rotates, switches the supply so that the rotational force is consistent, and the motor goes round.
DC motors have always been easier to control than AC motors, and are still a common sight in industrial and domestic applications. Most domestic washing machines now use DC motors and controllers; AC motors and controllers are still too expensive in this application - but see chapter 9. In industrial applications, the death of the DC drive and motor has long been predicted, and maybe is finally becoming reality as AC drives become dominant. However, there is a massive installed base of DC motors and drives, and many users are reluctant to 'upgrade' to AC, especially when their system is working reliably. DC drives are a mature design, and performance and reliability has long been more than adequate for most users. Where positioning and speed control are vital, and where high torque is needed at low speed, DC drives may still be specified.

What determines the Speed of a DC motor?

You'll remember from chapter 3 that, assuming we have energised the field winding of our motor, we can apply a voltage to the armature winding, a current will flow, and the armature and shaft will turn. A back EMF will be generated proportional to speed, and this will oppose the applied voltage so that:

Applied voltage = Back EMF + Voltage losses

Working things through in chapter 3, this became

$$\mathbf{V = K_a n\phi + IR} \qquad \mathbf{(3)}$$

(K_a is some constant, n is the speed, and ϕ the flux)
If these IR losses are small, then the rotational speed of the machine is proportional to the applied voltage, which is quite handy really.

In summary then, if we want to control the speed of the motor, we should control the voltage, and if we want to control or limit the torque, we should control or limit the armature current, because it is the current that makes torque. It's really that simple!

Current Compensation and Field Weakening

But we can make it more complicated. Not much though.
We saw that, with a fixed supply voltage, increasing the load slowed the motor a little, which led to increased current taking up the load. The voltage losses mainly come from the resistance of the armature windings and the armature current - the IR part of the equation above. Now it's pretty likely we are measuring the current in our controller and we probably know, (or can guess) the armature resistance of the motor.
Therefore, we can calculate the changing IR voltage drop for any load condition. It's not a work of genius now to increase the applied voltage slightly to compensate for this drop, restoring the speed to its original, unloaded value.
This method of improving speed regulation is unimaginatively called IR compensation, or even IR comp if you are in a hurry.

Finally, one last look at the equation tells us that, keeping everything else constant, if we increase the field (that is the flux ϕ), we will decrease the motor speed. This is pretty pointless as we know we can control the speed fairly easily and in any case if we try to push the field higher there is a good chance the iron in the field winding will saturate, things will get hot and we'll lose field anyway.
But how about reducing, or weakening the field? According to the equation, this will speed up the motor, all other things being equal, and so it does. So, once we have run out of armature voltage, because the mains supply voltage is limited, we can still go faster by reducing the field voltage. However, we don't get something for nothing, and, as the speed increases, the torque capability reduces as there is less field on the armature conductors for the same current. So, higher speed, lower torque. The power capability stays the same. Field weakening is useful in an application like a washing machine, where you need a high speed for spin, but not much torque; see chapter 9.

What do we need in a DC motor controller?

It's pretty clear now. We'll need a nice source of high power DC voltage that we can control and apply to the armature. We should measure the armature current so we can control torque, and do some IR compensation.

We'll need a field supply as well, and if we want to do field weakening we'll have to be able to control it. So let's consider the power part of the drive now, and how we'll use it.

The DC Drive

We saw in chapter 2 that there are several ways to control voltage in power electronics. Switched mode techniques such as buck and boost converters, switching at high frequencies, are ideal for low power applications such as computer power supplies. However, as we move into the kilowatt range of control, phase controlled rectifiers come into their own. There are several reasons for this. Thyristors were the first semiconductor devices that could handle the voltage and power needed for motor control, and are suited to phase control. They are extremely robust, and can be protected by high-speed fuses. Phase controlled drives had also been developed in the past using mercury arc rectifiers, so the concept was well understood. Also, the end product is the most cost effective DC drive solution – always a winning argument.

The principle of phase control rectification using thyristors is described in Chapter 2. As a reminder, just think of the thyristor as a controlled diode, which you can turn on whenever you want, but only turns off, like a diode, when the current falls to zero. By delaying the turn on (during the phase of the sine wave – hence phase control) we can have as much or as little voltage as we like from the supply.

So that's it then. Bear in mind that two thyristors need to conduct to get a current to flow, so they are turned on (gated) in pairs to match the phase sequencing. The actual circuitry for gating the thyristor is pretty simple and is described in the box. Deciding when you want to gate the thyristor is a bit more involved – see later.

Gate pulse drivers

A thyristor is a pretty simple device from the control point of view. To turn on, it needs a few volts applied to its gate (with respect to its Cathode) and, providing the current in the main device is high enough (called the latching current oddly enough) it will latch on and stay on until the current falls to zero. The thyristors are at supply potential, so to connect to the gates we need some form of isolation. They aren't even at the same potential. The top thyristors have their cathodes all common, but the bottom ones are connected to different AC input phases. As we only need a pulse to turn the thyristor on, a pulse transformer is a neat solution. We could use optocouplers, but we'd need a separate supply on the 'hot' side. A typical gate pulse circuit is shown below. Power electronic engineers like a nice big transformer so they can provide a long powerful pulse. One reason is that if the drive is running in discontinuous current it may take some time for the current in the thyristor to reach the latching current (the load being inductive and all that). There are various ways around this, but a long pulse from a big pulse transformer is a good solution.

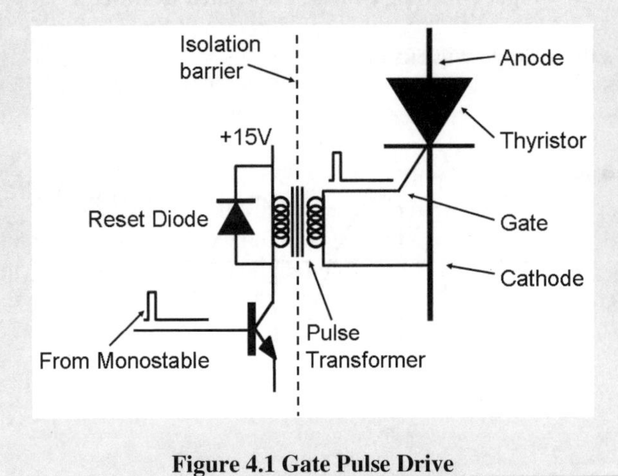

Figure 4.1 Gate Pulse Drive

So, a simple speed controller will consist of a thyristor rectifier bridge, some form of phase control circuitry and not much else. For simplicity let's look at a single phase controller first. Here's the basic circuit again of the phase controller. We'll need a supply for the field as well, but let's focus on the armature voltage supply.

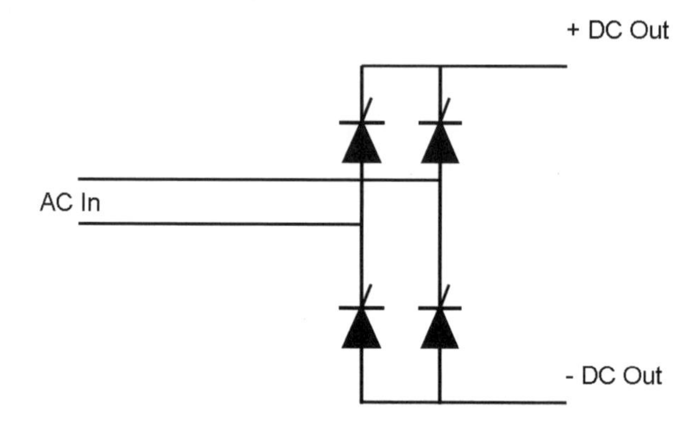

Figure 4.2 Single Phase Controlled Rectifier

And here's the voltage waveform.

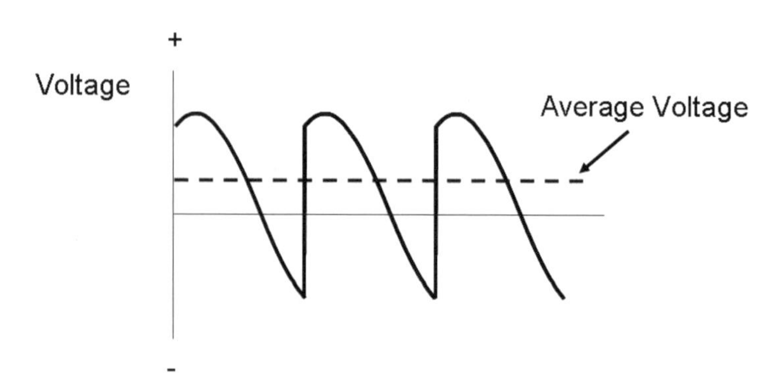

Figure 4.3 Controlled Rectifier Output Voltage

These waveforms assume an inductive and resistive load, and some supply inductance. Believe me, in the real world, there's inductance everywhere, you can't get away from it. Motors, chokes, cables, transformers – all are inductive to a greater or lesser extent.
In this first picture we are gating the thyristor (that is, turning it on) with a delay angle (α, alpha is usually used as the symbol for the delay angle) of about 60°. So the armature sees a reduced voltage, which would be zero if the delay angle were 180°. The resulting current is shown in the next figure.

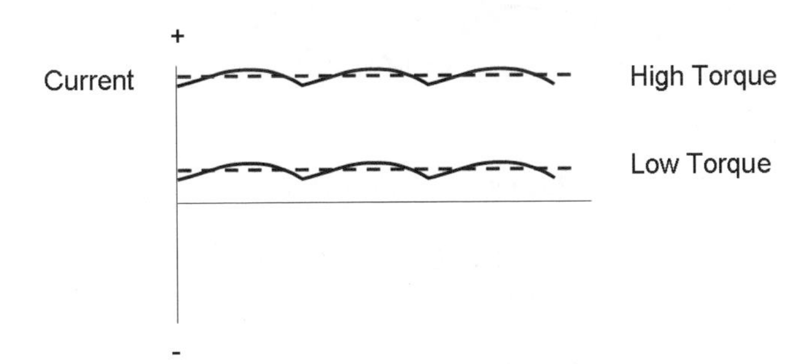

Figure 4.4 Controlled Rectifier Output Current – DC Motor load

As explained earlier, the average level of the current is dependent on the torque loading of the motor. The phase controlled voltage results in a ripple current that, because of the inductive load of the motor armature, rises sluggishly as the voltage rises, and rather reluctantly falls as the voltage reduces. Typical inductive load!
But perhaps what happens as the voltage passes through zero volts needs a little thought. The inductance keeps the current flowing, so the thyristor continues to conduct even though the voltage is now negative. In fact, it conducts until the next thyristor is gated, and the current switches, or is commutated as we say, from one thyristor to the other.
You'll recall that the speed of the motor is still determined basically by the voltage on the armature, so varying the delay angle α allows us to control the speed.
This all works pretty well, but….(there's always a but)
Let's look at what happens if we're running along at a nice speed, but the load is very low (maybe the drive belt snapped).

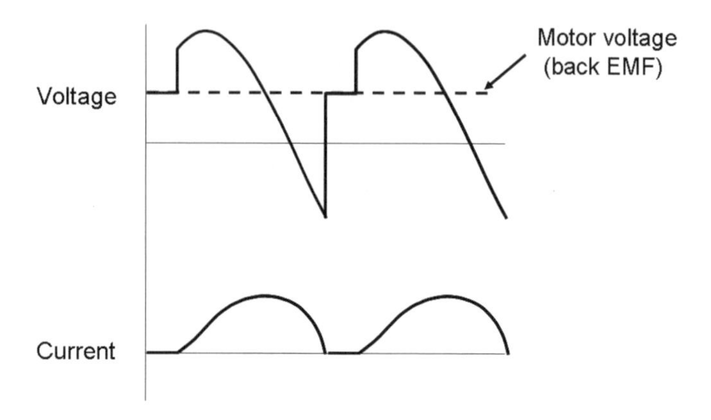

Figure 4.5 Discontinuous Current at Low Torque

Well, the current is so low it's falling to zero between voltage 'top ups'. It's *discontinuous,* as drives engineers would say. Also notice that, because the current is zero, the first thyristor has turned off earlier than before, and the resultant voltage waveform has changed. During this dead time, as the volts aren't defined by the input, they're showing the voltage (the back EMF) from the motor, which is freewheeling with no armature current for a few milliseconds. Now because this first thyristor has turned off before the next thyristor commutates it, the average voltage from the rectifier bridge is higher than when we had continuous current, with some negative voltage which was reducing the average voltage. If the volts are higher, then the speed is higher. So, if the motor is running along nicely and the drive belt snaps, the load reduces, the current correspondingly drops, and becomes discontinuous. If the phase controller has kept the delay angle α constant while this happens, suddenly the motor will speed up out of all proportion to the slight change you'd expect when you lost the load. Maybe your controller will catch up and increase α quickly, but clearly discontinuous current is not good.

We can prevent discontinuous current by putting additional inductance in the armature supply, or, more usually by going for a six pulse three phase bridge, so the sine waves come thick and fast, the current ripple is a much higher frequency, and lower amplitude. Obviously the average current (torque, load) can now fall to a lot lower value before discontinuous current occurs. Three phase systems are also much better suited than single phase systems to the higher powers we usually associate with drives.

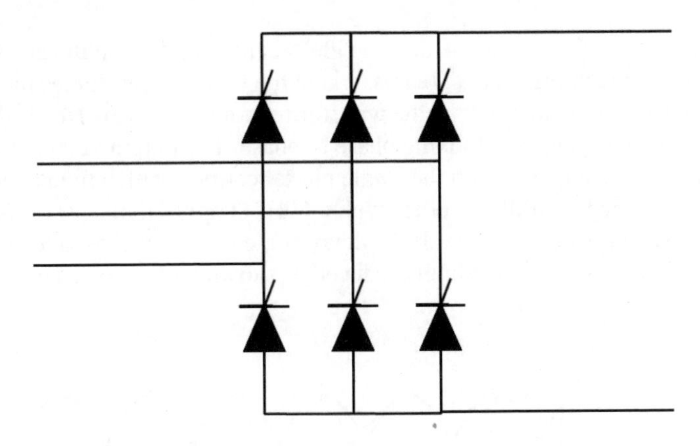

Figure 4.6 three phase controlled Rectifier

The Three Phase Controller Rectifier

As these phase controllers form the basis of most DC drives, let's look more closely at the voltage waveforms for different delay angles, α.

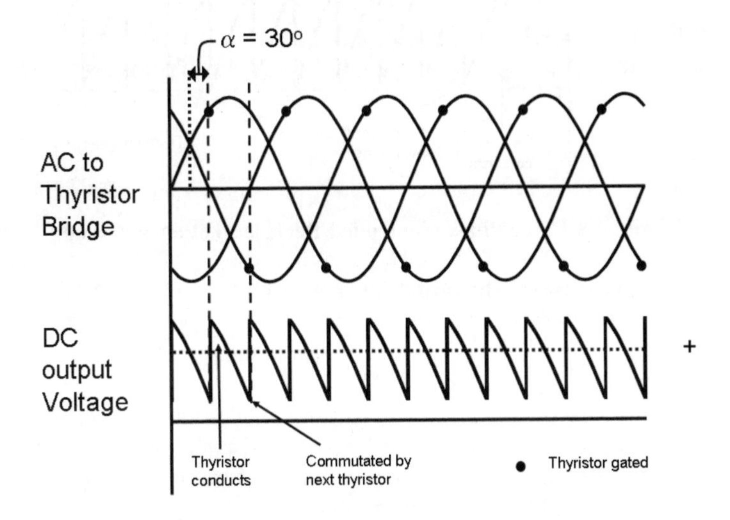

Figure 4.7 Three Phase Controlled Rectifier Voltages, α = 30°

First thing to notice is that the delay angle α is measured from the crossing point of the incoming phases; that is, where the one phase becomes more positive (or in the other half of the waveform, more negative). This is the zero crossing if you were looking phase to phase. The output voltage has a lot less ripple compared with the single phase rectifier, with a fundamental ripple frequency of 300Hz (360Hz with a 60Hz supply); that is, six times the supply frequency of 50Hz. If the delay angle is now increased to 60° the output voltage is correspondingly reduced as shown in the next figure.

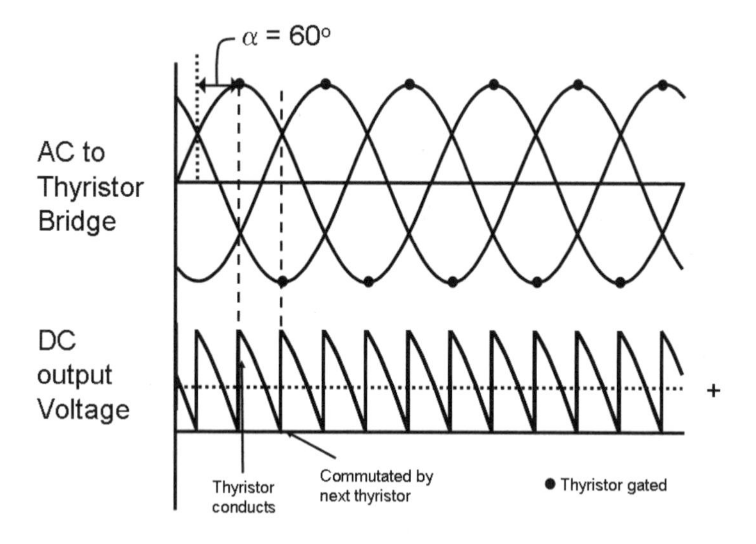

Figure 4.8 Three Phase Controlled Rectifier Voltages, α = 60°

Logically the next figure shows a delay angle of 90°

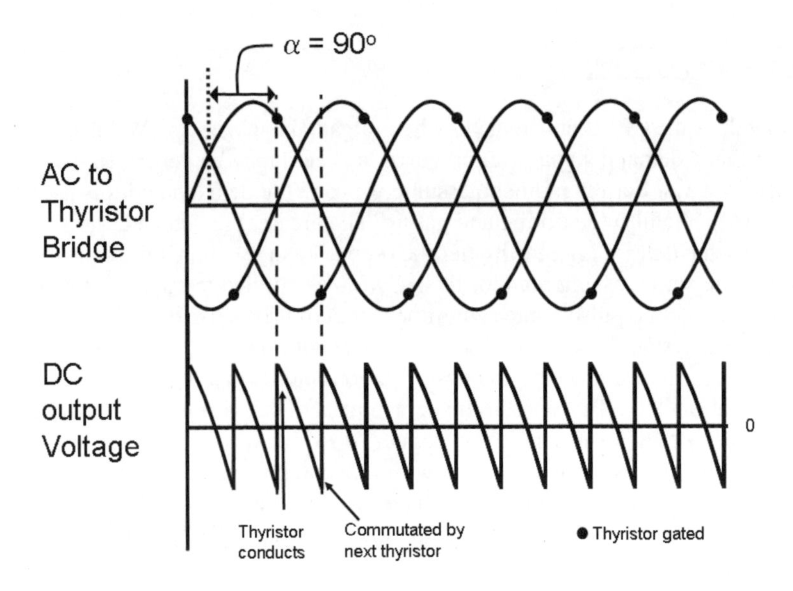

Figure 4.9 Three Phase Controlled Rectifier Voltages, a = 90°

What's happening now is the output voltage is positive and negative, giving a net value of zero. Remember, we have an inductive load that will keep the current flowing in a pair of thyristors until the next pair commutate it and take over, so at large delay angles we'll get an output voltage that becomes increasingly negative. The actual delay angle is calculated from the zero crossing point; for an explanation of how this circuitry used to work, see box: **Timing and Gating**.

Timing and Gating

How does the CPU know exactly when to gate the thyristors? We'll see later that a demand signal (i.e for a certain speed) may be generated in various ways. For the moment, assume we have the demand and it is used to drive (eventually) the timing and gating. The greater the demand, the smaller the delay angle, the higher the output voltage. The CPU needs to know the zero crossing point of the AC voltage applied to the thyristor so it can generate the pulse at the right time. Modern drives use digital phase lock loop systems to ensure accurate timing, with sophisticated software to account for interference, frequency variations etc. Armed with this information, the CPU looks at the demand, calculates a suitable delay angle, and generates a pulse. That's the wonder of software.
It's maybe interesting to look at how timing and pulse generation was done in the past. In the figure below, we have a timing transformer that supplies a low voltage reference sine wave, hopefully in phase with that going to the thyristor bridge.

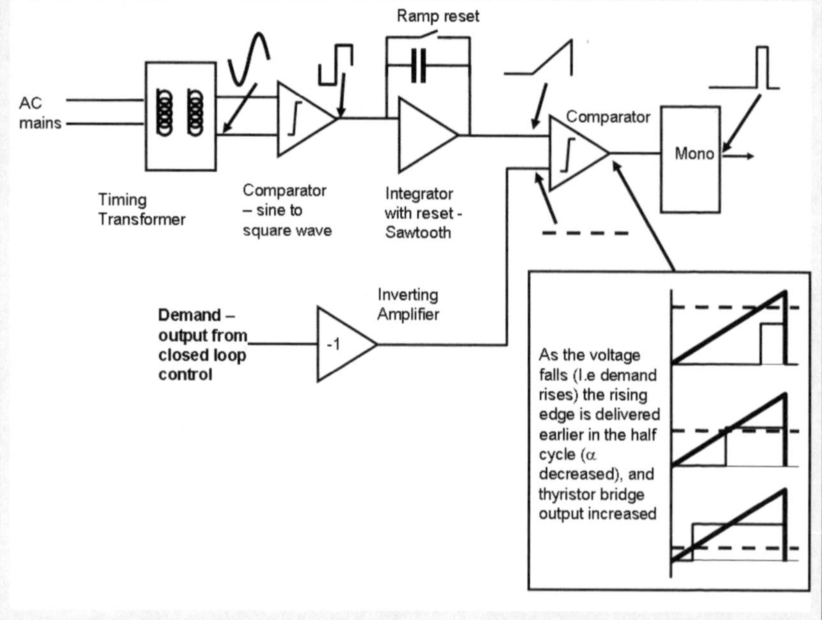

Figure 4.10 Gate pulse timing – the old fashioned way

The signal from the transformer is used to generate a sawtooth waveform using a comparator to square up the sine wave, then a simple integrator to produce the rising ramp. The ramp is reset by the falling edge of the comparator output (not shown). The sawtooth is then compared with the demand signal (negative for more demand in this case, so there's an inverting amplifier in the demand input) and the resultant edge used to trigger a monostable to produce a pulse. The pulse connects to the gate amplifier and pulse transformer as described earlier. Remember in reality we are dealing with a three phase system and six thyristors that need accurate gating in pairs.

However, while this is easy to understand, it is an analogue system and subject to noise and inaccuracy. Also, the inevitable phase shift in the timing transformer would lead to slight errors, usually limiting the delay angle to a minimum value.
Either way, digital or analogue, a pulse is produced at the right time, according to the demand and delivered to the appropriate thyristor through a driver and pulse transformer as described earlier.

What's the motor doing?
So, we are messing around with the delay angle, increasing and decreasing the voltage on the motor. What's happening in practice? Well, we know the motor speed will follow the applied voltage pretty well. However, common sense tells us if we increase the armature voltage rapidly the motor won't accelerate instantly, then there will be a big gap between the back EMF and the applied voltage, and, as we saw earlier, a lot of current will flow supplying torque to accelerate the motor. At this point it may be handy to have some form of current limit that cuts in to protect the motor and drive, and this is of course what happens in most cases. If you have a high inertia load such as a fan, or (heaven forbid!) a centrifuge, then it's usual to sit in current limit accelerating the load as fast as possible – maybe for several minutes or more. Add the normal (steady) load to the accelerating load and you certainly need your current limit. Bear in mind that, to control current, you'll be controlling the voltage by adjusting the delay angle, α, but more of that when we talk about closed loop controllers.

What happens when we decelerate the motor? We reduce the voltage, we may even take it negative with a high delay angle. The motor and load are now decelerating, but our thyristor bridge cannot conduct negative current, so the torque – that is current - remains positive, but probably falls to zero.

In effect, there is now no driving or braking torque, so we cannot slow the motor rapidly unless we use a mechanical brake, or do something a little clever…

Forward and Reversing, Motoring and Generating

Motors can go forward or reverse, and they can motor or generate. Now with a DC motor, if we want it to go backwards, we simply need to reverse the field, or reverse the armature voltage. If we want it to generate, we'll need to reverse the current.
However, let's not confuse things. How about just reversing direction first? Well, we could reverse the field, but, although the field is relatively low power, it is very high inductance (it's a magnetic field – inductance and all that), so stopping the current, reversing the supply and starting again isn't so easy. Better to actually reverse the armature supply. OK, but how? Easy! Get a big changeover switch, capable of handling DC and switch it over and away you go. Cost of a fancy switch, some control electronics, and you have a forward and reverse DC drive.

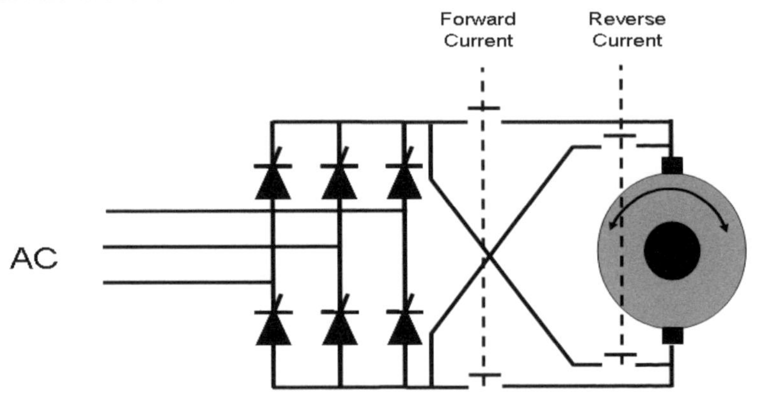

Figure 4.11 Reversing Switch

What's the catch? Firstly, it's not recommended to switch DC when you've got a lot of current, so it's advisable to slow down or otherwise reduce the load so the current is zero. Now you can switch over and start applying voltage to the armature again, this time causing it to run in reverse.
This process can take a few hundred milliseconds or more, so it's not ideal for fast processes. Also, if the motor is still spinning, the thyristor bridge will see a negative armature voltage, so you must be sure to put a lot of delay angle on the thyristors or you'll be popping fuses as the motor back EMF and applied voltages add, rather than subtract as usual. This resultant high voltage has only the armature resistance to limit current, so the braking (breaking!... Ha Ha!) torque could be potentially very high. Incidentally, the delay angle mustn't go too far under these circumstances in any case or you'll be popping fuses again as commutation from one thyristor to another doesn't work in the extreme.

Four Quadrant Operation

Let's look a bit more carefully at what happens as we go forward and reverse with, say a load like a lift, or elevator as they say in the US. Let's not try to work out what the voltage and current looks like in detail, we'll just draw nice level DC. Remember we can get a negative voltage out of a phase control bridge, but not a negative current. The four possible operating modes are shown in the figure below, which has four quadrants, so we talk about one, two, or four quadrant operation (three doesn't really work).

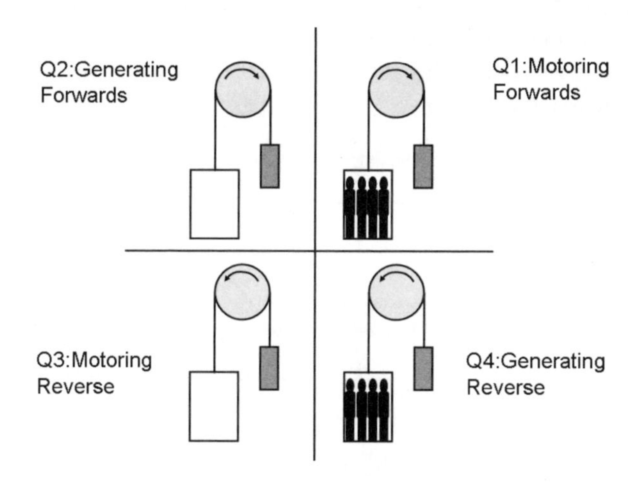

Figure 4.12 Four Quadrant Operation

Notice that the lift has a counterweight to reduce the overall load, so when the lift car is empty, the counterweight is dominant, and when the car is full, the car is the heavier component. Consider each quadrant in turn.

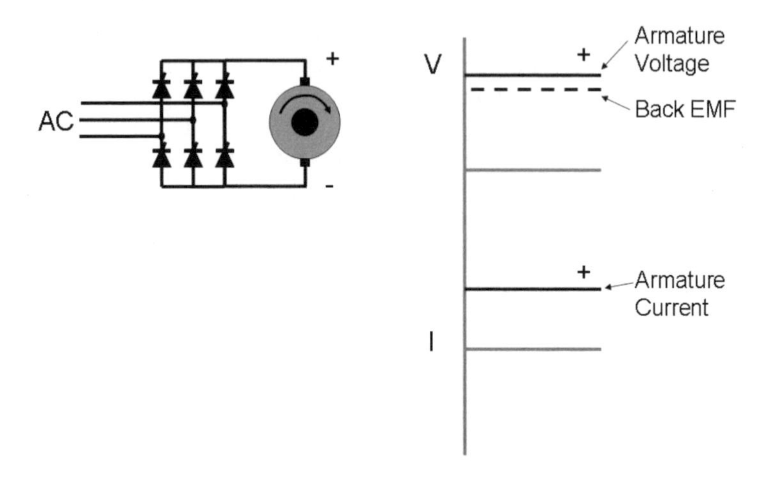

Figure 4.13 Q1: Motoring Forwards

Q1 is the easy case. The lift picks up a wedding party on the ground floor. We are motoring forwards, the armature voltage is positive and higher than the back EMF. The armature current is also positive, and producing a positive torque to lift the passengers in the car.
Now everyone gets out the lift at the reception on the fifth floor, but the lift carries on up to the tenth.

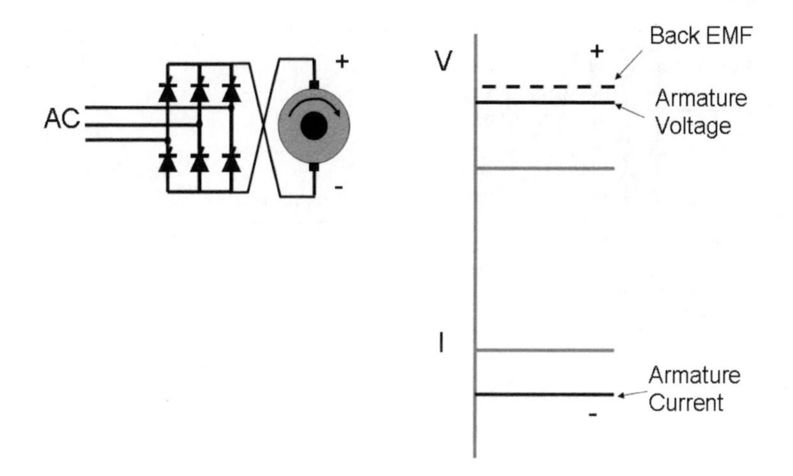

Figure 4.14 Q2: Generating Forwards

In Q2 the counterweight is now lifting the empty lift, and we are gaining energy from it as the counterweight falls. That is, we have negative torque, negative current, still going forwards – generating. To control this negative current we need to reverse our controller and allow the current to return to the supply. To look at it another way, the voltage is positive and the current negative, so the power (V x -I = -P) is negative. The graph in the figure also shows how the armature voltage is now less than the back emf, which explains the negative current. The graph represents the motor voltage and current of course; the thyristor bridge has been reversed so it sees the current as positive.

In Q3 the guy on the tenth floor that called the lift has forgotten his wallet and goes back to his room. So the lift arrives, waits and then goes down again empty.

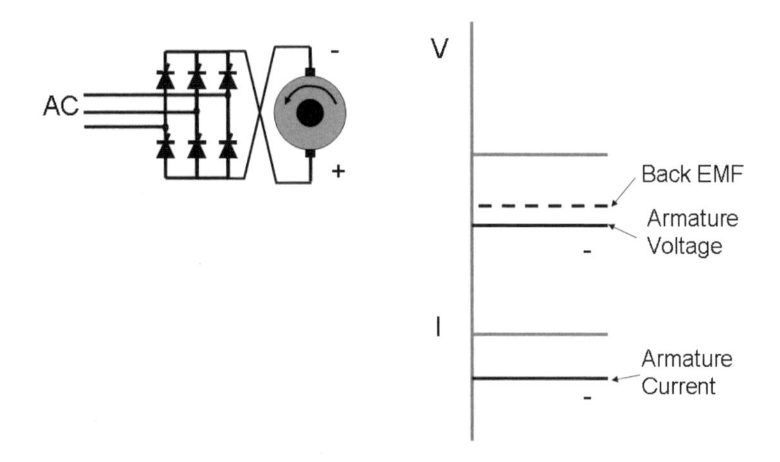

Figure 4.15 Q3: Motoring in Reverse

The motor is now reversed, and is lifting the counterweight. It's OK; everything is negative. The bridge is still reversed, the motor is reversing, and the armature voltage and current are negative. It's like Q1 but upside down. Of course the power is positive, as you'd expect (-V x -I = +P)

Finally, at the ground floor, Japanese tourists get in the lift to go to the orientation meeting in the basement.

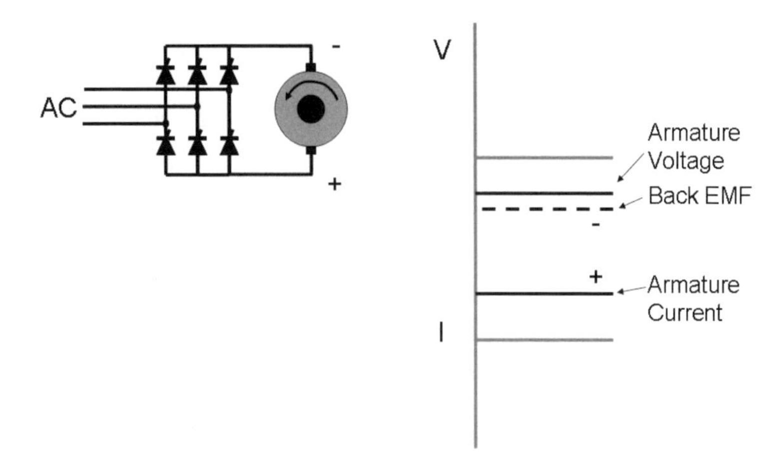

Figure 4.16 Q4: Generating in Reverse

Q4; the motor is still reversed, but the weight of the car is generating again. So we need to switch the thyristor bridge around again to allow current to go back to the supply.

It's clear in this application that we need to operate a lift in all four quadrants. Drives to do this are called Regenerative (Regen) drives. Switching the bridge around in a regen drive like this will take time. An alternative solution is to have two thyristor bridges, which we can use as required. Clearly control here has to be good; usually we'll fit some reactors to limit circulating currents between the bridges. This is called a double bridge regenerative drive. But this is getting a bit complicated.

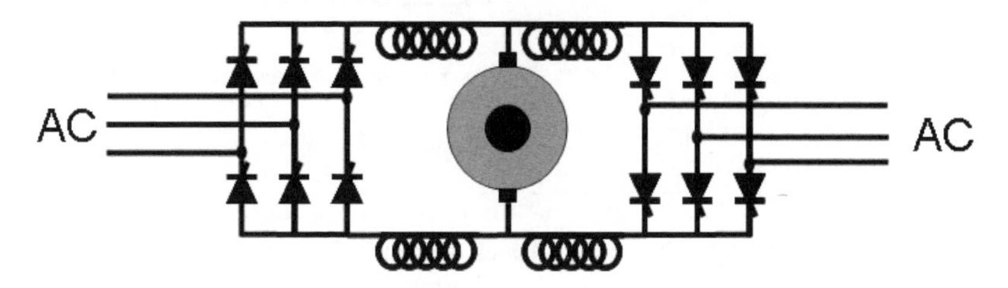

Figure 4.17 Double Bridge Regenerative Drive

DC Drives – A Practical Design

The thyristor DC drive is a pretty mature product, but it has been continuously updated and is packed full of the latest components and plenty of features. Early (and low cost) designs had various pre-set potentiometers to adjust current limit, acceleration etc. but these have now been replaced by programmable systems, and nearly all DC Drives have Microprocessors and the threat of software bugs, updates etc. We'll discuss how the drive is controlled in chapter 6, but let's focus here on the power circuitry.

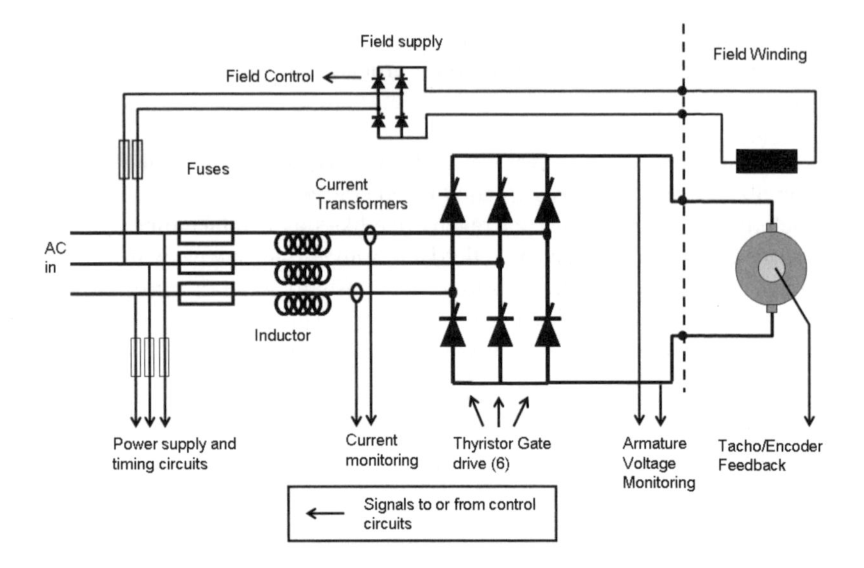

Figure 4.18 DC Drive – Block diagram Power section

AC In

The drive is connected to a three phase supply, usually 400V or so, with possible variations as described in chapter 1. As mentioned before, supplies can vary a lot from this nominal value, which makes for tricky selection of the thyristor voltage ratings, and doesn't help when designing the auxiliary power supplies either. Transients, brown outs (a short mains break, as opposed to a blackout) etc. further add to the confusion, and are discussed in Chapter 10. Suffice to say these can easily damage anything and everything in a drive. See below.

Fuses

We may be dealing with hundreds of kilowatts in a DC Drive, so fusing is absolutely critical. As mentioned in chapter 2, Thyristors are unusual in that they can be protected by suitable, expensive fuses (but not as expensive as the thyristors themselves). So fusing is fitted as standard, and separate fusing is provided to other parts of the drive.

Input Inductors

Input inductors are fitted on DC (and AC) drives for several reasons. Firstly, they will limit energy from the supply into the drive in the event of a supply transient or fault in the drive. Surges in power, either transients from switching, or high energy lightning strikes can cause damage to the thyristors, the control electronics or both. An inductor will limit the surge energy (because the surge is usually a high frequency event and the inductor therefore has a high impedance). Fitting an inductor is good practice with all drives, if only for this reason. A second reason for fitting an inductor on a DC drive is to prevent commutation notches from the drive entering the supply and causing problems in other equipment – like AC drives. These are explained in detail later, but suffice to say an inductor is pretty necessary here. Inductors also reduce harmonics (see chapter 10) by reducing peak currents (see chapter 2) and limit rates of rise of current in the thyristor bridge, although this isn't a problem with modern thyristors.

Current Transformers

Two current transformers are fitted to two of the input phases to monitor the bridge current, and therefore the armature current. You only need two transformers because you can calculate the third as all the currents must add up to zero at any one time. I mean, where else is the current going to go? Current transformers (CTs) are widely used in electrical systems. They are doughnut shaped toroids which look nothing like a voltage transformer but work on the same principle. The primary winding goes through the middle, usually a heavy cable carrying the current we wish to measure. This is a single turn winding, and the secondary is wound around the toroid, maybe one thousand turns. So if we have 100A in the primary, we'll get 100mA in the secondary. Stick a little resistor on the secondary and you'll get an isolated voltage signal faithfully reproducing the primary current. Like any transformer, it works only with AC. Unlike a voltage transformer, it must have a load, because with a primary current of 100A it's going to push out 100mA come what may, even if it means generating a plasma. Open circuit CTs are the sort of things that start fires.... CTs are often fitted with a local, safety resistor to prevent this.

Thyristor Bridge

This is the key part of the drive. The thyristors themselves are available in many different sizes and packages, ranging from little TO220 packs, isolated two, four and six packs, to large, disc like 'hockey puck' devices for really high power.

Most low and intermediate power devices are mounted in isolated packs as discussed in chapter 2, often in pairs, with the centre point connection already joined. This makes it a lot easier to mount them on a large single heatsink at earth potential.

Why a heatsink? Well, we saw earlier that all semiconductors lose heat when they are carrying current, and thyristors are no exception. A thyristor exhibits a typical drop of a volt or so. Not much, until you put a few hundred Amps through it. Most semiconductors fail at 125°C or 150°C, hence the need for heatsinks, fans, temperature monitors, cooling air, filters, air conditioning systems etc. A whole technology of cooling. The drive may therefore also incorporate a cooling fan control circuit and heatsink temperature monitor.

Back to the thyristor stack, as it's sometimes called. On a small drive, a PCB may sit directly on top of the isolated packs, carrying drive circuits and power connections. For higher powers, copper busbars may be fitted directly to the packs, and a PCB mounted on top. Busbars can then take the DC directly to the output terminals and to the motor.

Armature Voltage Monitoring

So far, CTs or pulse transformers have isolated all our signals from the power part to the control. To monitor the armature voltage we can use a nice high impedance voltage divider feeding a differential amplifier into our A to D converter. The higher impedance the better here, as we are connecting the industrial mains to our control circuit, microprocessor, and the user's control terminals. A small leakage current is acceptable, but if we have lots of drives in a system, the leakage may be sufficient to compromise leakage monitors (see chapter 7). In this case, isolation amplifiers are needed, at great expense.

Field Supply

The field supply is usually only single phase, so we can save a bit of money on components, and the field is such a big inductor we don't need to worry about ripple currents. If we want to do field weakening, we'll need thyristors instead of diodes, together with pulse transformers again. Monitoring of current and voltage may also be necessary.

Tacho and Encoder feedback

Early drives used Tachometers to measure the actual speed of the motor. A tacho is a small DC generator designed for this purpose. It's quite expensive, as getting the tacho to produce a linear voltage signal, proportional to speed over a wide speed range is harder than you think. Tachos have been replaced now by encoders, which are described in chapter 8. Encoder signals need processing and scaling, but will provide a reliable indication of motor speed and direction.

The use of feedback brings us nicely to the control part of the DC drive, but before we move on to the control circuit, we need to consider a couple of problems that the drive may cause to the supply and other equipment.

Practical Matters - Commutation Spikes

Remember how we showed that a thyristor continued to conduct until the next thyristor takes over or commutates it? Well, it's not quite that simple. The act of commutation forces the current in the thyristor to zero with quite a thump, and this looks uncommonly like a short circuit to the supply, albeit for a short time. To stop this surge of current going all over the plant, DC drives are usually fitted with an input inductor, (imaginatively called a commutation choke) which will limit any surge currents at the expense of a notch in the voltage on the drive side. Notches still get through, and can cause serious interference in other electrical and electronic equipment. Like other drives for example.

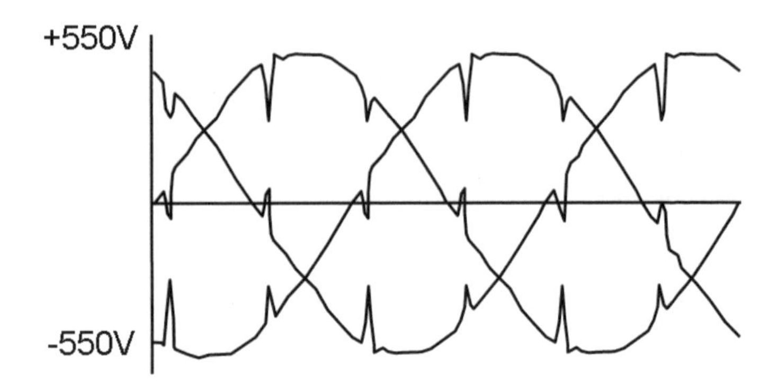

Figure 4.19 Notches in supply caused by Thyristor Commutation

Commutation chokes are neither large nor expensive, and can be supplied by the drive manufacturer or third parties - who are usually cheaper.

Practical Matters – Harmonics and 12 Pulse Systems

When the electrical supply system was put together, most of the loads were nice sinusoidal ones – resistive, inductive or a mixture of the two. So loading up the system didn't really cause too many difficulties. However, when we come along and fit a big thyristor drive to the supply, we take chunks of current out of the sine wave and generally cause distortion. This leads to problems with transformers and other equipment, and is discussed in more detail in chapter 10. In order to try to reduce this, DC drive manufacturers came up with several ideas. Fitting an input choke as described above helps by smoothing the current taken by the drive, but higher power drives can really start causing serious distortion. A rather expensive solution is the so called twelve pulse drive, shown in the figure below.

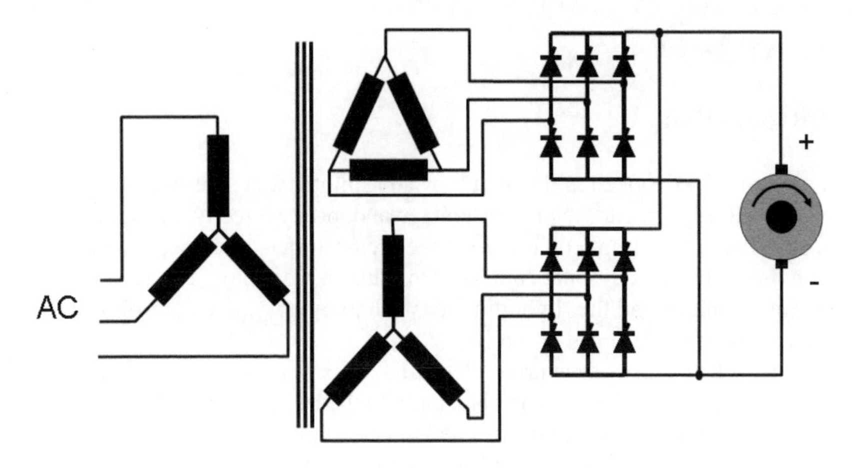

Figure 4.20 Twelve Pulse Thyristor Drive

The transformer has two secondary windings, one star and one delta connected, which create a six phase supply with 30° between each phase. Twelve thyristors are used, so now the drive now takes current every 30° Instead of every 60°, so the distortion is less, and the harmonics greatly reduced. However, we now have 12 thyristors (for a single quadrant drive) as well as a fancy Star/Delta transformer, so things are getting expensive and complicated. Think of the timing for the thyristor gating. Twelve pulse drives come into their own above (say) 200kW, but some water authorities will specify them to quite low powers to prevent harmonic problems.

This is all getting a bit complicated now, so let's look at AC drives, and then we'll talk about control of both DC and AC.

Summary

DC drives use thyristors to control the armature voltage and therefore the speed of the motor; IR compensation improves the speed holding without the need of feedback. Phase control is a little tricky, what with discontinuous current and commutation notches, and four quadrant operation requires extra circuitry and control. DC drives are pretty mature and reliable these days, with isolated thyristor packs, heatsinks and associated circuitry.

5. AC Drives

Introduction

In chapter 4 we looked in detail at how a DC motor was controlled using a thyristor bridge to vary the motor voltage and, pretty directly, the speed. Controlling the current could control the motor torque, and a separate field winding allowed additional control of the flux in the motor. The simple motor equations and the 'light dimmer' technology of phase control made for simple, reliable speed control.
We'll see that many of the principles of motor control, such as four quadrant operation, field weakening etc. also apply to the control of an AC motor. However, as we saw in chapter 3, the industry standard induction motor is very different to the shunt wound DC motor, or any other DC motor for that matter.

Just to recap:

- AC induction or asynchronous motors are easy and cheap to construct, consisting of a wound stator on the outside, and a simple, cast, 'squirrel cage' rotor.
- The speed of the motor is largely determined by the applied frequency (and the number of pole pairs), although the motor will always run a little slower than synchronous speed, due to slip.
- The motor flux is dependent on the applied voltage, and this must be controlled in order to optimise torque but prevent saturation of the iron.
- Motors can be reversed by swapping phases, and can regenerate from a load that returns energy to the motor
- Motors are built with standard power ratings, normally to an IEC or NEMA standard.

Controller Requirements

From the above it should be clear that to control the speed of the motor we will need to control the frequency of the three phase supply feeding it. We will also need to control the applied voltage, because this will determine the motor flux. The motor torque is a product of the flux and the motor current, so we should be ready to control the current as well.

Some motors are fitted with temperature sensors or trips to protect the motor against overheating, but as we are monitoring the current, maybe our controller can provide some protection against overload as well.
Any good piece of power electronics is short circuit proof, and we'll see that we'll need to protect the controller against overvoltages if the motor regenerates.
So we need a variable frequency, variable voltage, three phase controller which is short circuit and over voltage protected, and which can control the current in the motor if necessary. Our controller has to work with the voltages, currents and powers associated with industrial motors – from a hundred to maybe several Megawatts.

The Variable Voltage, Variable Frequency Inverter

We saw in chapter 2 that AC can be turned into DC by simple rectification using a diode bridge. We also saw that DC could be turned back into AC by a process of inversion using some form of electronic switch, such as an IGBT. We can control the output voltage by varying the pulse width (PWM – Pulse Width Modulation), but we'd better have some com diodes to take the inductive load currents when the IGBTs are switched off.
Now it's just a question of changing the clock rate, and we can speed up or slow down the process and vary the frequency of the square wave.
However, if we want to control the speed of an AC motor, there are a couple of things wrong here. As we are producing a square wave voltage, the currents in the motor are going to be nothing like a sine wave, and full of harmonics causing losses, and not giving smooth, steady torque. Also, the motor requires a three-phase supply with the correct phase sequence in order to operate properly.
If we are prepared to switch the IGBTs on and off more frequently, we could generate a pattern of pulses that, if filtered, would produce a sine wave voltage, as shown in the figure below. The motor inductance won't have any effect on the voltage pulses coming out of the inverter, but the current in the motor will be smoothed by the inductance and will begin to look a bit like a sine wave, which is what matters to the motor. Clearly the more often you switch, the more pulses you produce, and the current shape gets closer to a true sine wave.

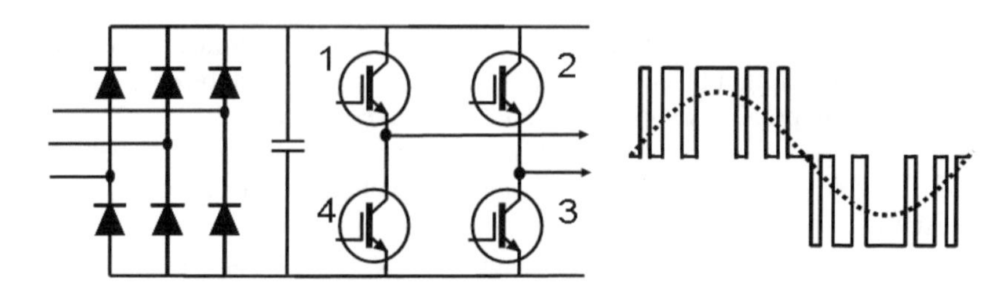

Figure 5.1 Sine Wave Pulse Width Modulation

It's important to realise that the voltage is still a series of square waves, even though the inductance of the motor smoothes the current to something approaching a sine wave. We'll look at this more closely later.
The commutation diodes are now pretty important, as the IGBTs are switching on and off all the time, and the inductive current must continue to flow via the com diodes.
We are still operating a single phase inverter, so let's add a couple more IGBTs and com diodes, so we finally arrive at our fully functional three phase inverter, shown below.

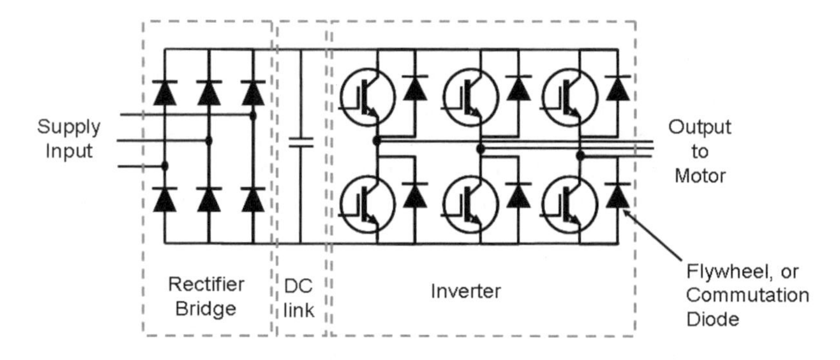

Figure 5.2 Variable Voltage, Variable Frequency Inverter

Incidentally, what do we call this? Saying Drive, or AC Drive is often taken to include the motor; Converter or Controller are pretty general names. Our American colleagues like to talk about Variable Speed (or Frequency) Drives, inevitably abbreviated to VSD or VFD. Inverter strictly refers to the business end, connected to the motor, converting DC to AC.

However, all these terms are used interchangeably to describe what I'll refer as the Drive or Inverter.

Some more definitions; Output and Switching Frequencies

The *Output* frequency is the frequency of the three phase current waveform that drives the motor. The motor is designed to be connected to the normal mains supply, so it's expecting a frequency of 50 or 60Hz. Most inverters will produce an output from 0Hz to at least 300Hz, and in many cases up to 600Hz or more. This permits use with exotic motors designed for these high speeds, but we'll see later these are unusual, and few applications take the motor above 100Hz.

The *Switching* frequency is the frequency at which the IGBTs are turned on and off. In some early designs this was an exact multiple of the output frequency – that is, the two were synchronised. However, modern designs avoid this limitation and operate with a fixed switching frequency, which is more convenient in digital systems, and also simplifies the design of any EMC filters that are needed (Chapter 10). Ideally, a switching frequency of above 20kHz would be desirable, as any acoustic noise produced would be inaudible (except to dogs). At this high frequency a highly accurate sine wave can be produced, minimizing motor losses. However, switching losses at these frequencies will be prohibitively high, except for very low power or low voltage inverters, so switching frequencies are usually between 2 and 8kHz for higher power drives, while lower power, lower voltage (230V AC input) may switch at 16kHz or more. The user can usually select switching frequencies, and we'll see in chapter 9 why. Actually, the acoustic noise from the drive is predominately double switching frequency under load, so noise isn't so much of a problem, except in applications such as air conditioning.

Currents and Voltages at the Output

We've added the extra IGBTs to make a three phase inverter, but we need to look more closely at the output voltage and current paths in the inverter itself. Let's think about how the pulse width modulated waveform will build up the three phase, sine wave currents the motor wants:

- You can't have a top and bottom IGBT in the same leg on at the same time – this will give a short circuit across the DC link.
- You must provide a current path through the motor winding by turning on top and bottom devices (in different legs!) at the same time.
- Actually you need to provide three current paths – one for each winding, and these need to be phase displaced like a real three phase waveform.

There are also some practical limitations:

- As stated above, you can't switch on and off at too high a frequency as there are losses from switching and the IGBTs would get too hot.
- However, you should choose a reasonably high switching frequency to build up a nice sine wave current, particularly at high motor frequencies.
- You need to make sure you have as high an output voltage as possible; the DC link is limited to the peak of the supply voltage, and this should be your peak output voltage (i.e. 400V or 230V AC in, 400V or 230V AC out).
- You must allow a very short time or 'deadband' between turning a top IGBT off and turning the bottom one on (and vice versa), as IGBTs take time to turn off and you don't want a short circuit or 'shoot through' current
- You shouldn't try to generate very narrow pulses for the same reason.

There are other problems related to switching such as losses in the flywheel diodes, and generating Electromagnetic Interference (EMI), which we'll look at later.

Modulation methods

Before we look at the way we drive the IGBTs on and off, we need to decide on the modulation method. Many PhDs have been gained proposing modulation methods, because we can't just generate sine waves at U, V and W, as shown in the figure below.

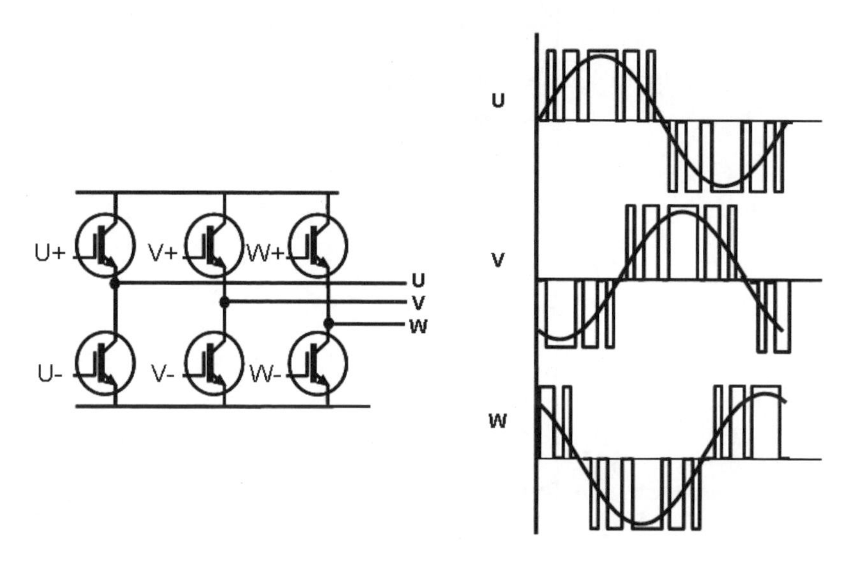

Figure 5.3 Simple Sine Wave Modulation

Here, each IGBT produces a nice sine wave (i.e. a series of square waves which would average to a sine wave) for 180°, and then turns off while its partner does the same. The problem here is that the peak to peak value of the sine wave would be the same as the DC link voltage, which is half what we need to operate the motor at 50 or 60Hz. (Think about it. The supply is say 400V AC. We rectify it and get about 560V from the peak sensing of the capacitor. A peak to peak sine wave of 560V is just 200V AC) We need more volts.

This is where the PhDs come in. One solution is use a modulation pattern shown in the figure below. Here we've looked at the modulation pattern for each IGBT – we'll see why later.

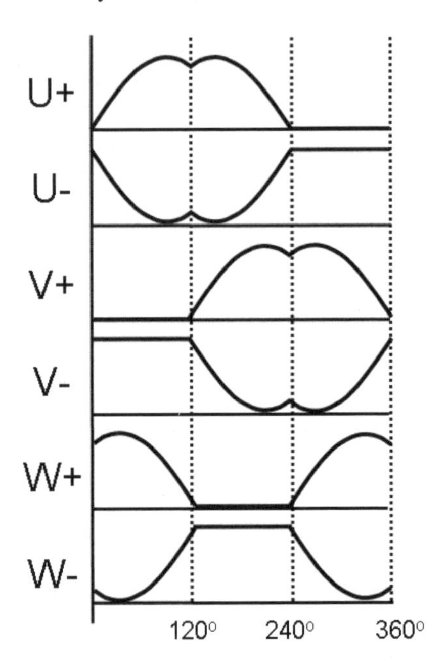

Figure 5.4 Fixed, Low side Bias Modulation

With these waveforms, you can see how the voltage is generated by considering the voltage between any two phases at any one time. In the first 120°, U+ is sine wave modulated, and is conducting to V-, which is on all the time, connecting to the DC link negative. So a nice average sine wave is produced, rising at its peak to the DC link value.
Similarly, W+ is also conducting to V-, and is sine wave modulated, but 120° out of phase with U, which is correct. With a little imagination, you can see that W+ and U- (both parts of sine waves) will conduct to form another sine wave voltage, suitably 120° displaced from the other two.

In the second 120° of the cycle, U+ to V- will conduct (now a sine wave minus another), the *difference* continuing the nice smooth sine wave started in the first 120°. And so on. As the cycle proceeds, sine waves are generated either by subtracting one sine wave from the other, or by modulating, using a sine wave, with respect to the DC link, positive or negative.
But looking at waveforms like this is a little confusing. For a start, U+ and U- appear to be on at the same time, and other conduction paths and voltages are apparent which I haven't pointed out. The answer is to remember that we are not dealing with analogue voltages (i.e. as drawn) here; these waveforms represent a pattern of pulses, which, *if averaged*, would look like these waveforms. The time separation will take care of these problems.
Incidentally, I worked out this modulation method for myself many years ago (re-inventing the wheel as usual) and called it Fat Ladies Bottom modulation, due to the shape. I apologise for the sexism, but this was a long time ago. The initials have come into use in some literature, but are more diplomatically referred to as Fixed Low side Biasing, or something similar.

Pulses in a Window

Let's see how we generate a 50Hz output frequency with a switching frequency of 8kHz. In each half cycle of 10ms there will be 80 pulses, so we'll get a pretty good sine wave. If we look at particular window of 125us, we can see what's happening to the conduction paths.

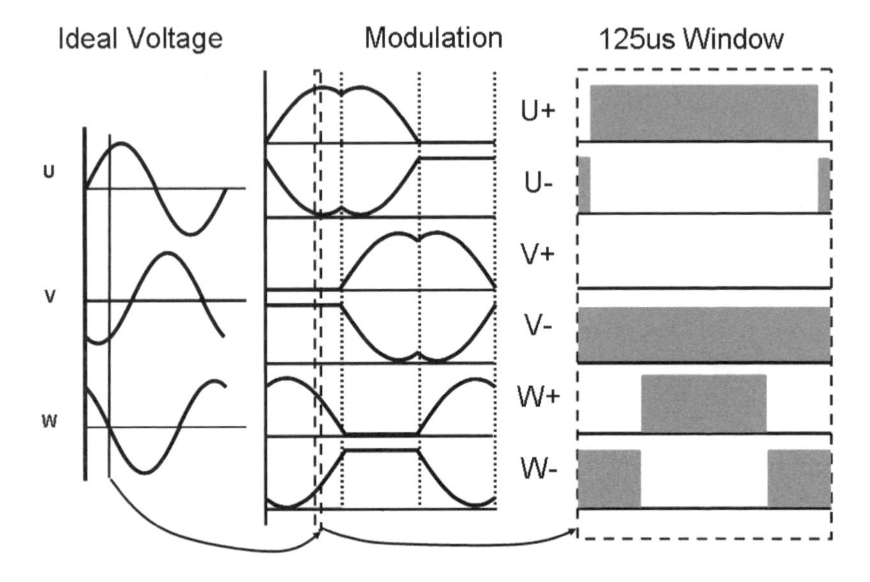

Figure 5.5 Pulses in the Inverter

Maybe now it's a little clearer. IGBT U+ is on for a long time during this window, and V- is on all the time, so there is a high average voltage across the U and V motor phases. W+ is conducting for a long time to V-, but not as much as U+; this corresponds to the average voltages we expect. Finally, U+ is conducting to W-, providing a relatively low voltage and conduction path.
Notice that the pulse positions are important to provide the current paths; it's not just enough to decide a particular pulse width is needed to produce a voltage, it must correspond to another device being on as well.

Other Modulation Methods

This is just the tip of the iceberg when it comes to modulation methods. Academic careers seem to be built on new ways of varying pulse widths to control motors. Oddly enough though, commercial drives seem to limit themselves to relatively simple methods of control. One popular modulation method is known as Space Vector Modulation. The modulation pattern is shown in the diagram below.

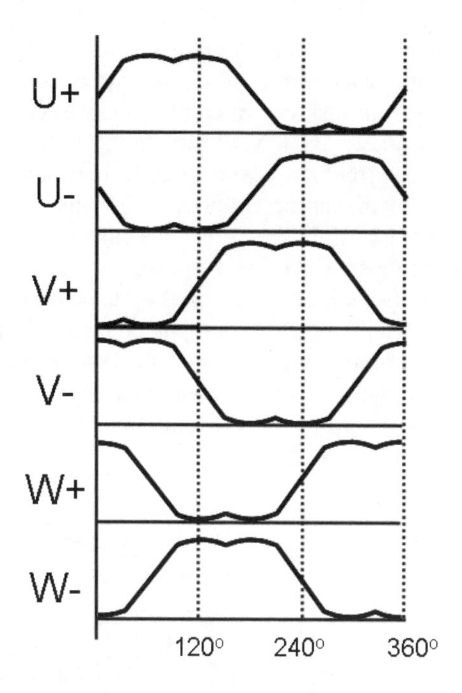

Figure 5.6 Space Vector Modulation

Space Vector Modulation (SVC) is similar to FLB, but the modulation pattern is continuous. In FLB one phase is always clamped to the link, the other two modulate to it and one another. With SVC, all devices are switching all of the time, and the modulation pattern makes it difficult to see how the sine wave comes out. But it does.

Hysteresis current control (HCC) uses a rather different control principle. We know we eventually want a sinusoidal current; the voltage doesn't really matter. So we set a reference sinewave current, and we set upper and lower boundaries from that sinewave. Now we turn on our IGBTs watch the current (say) rise. The current rises exponentially, depending on the inductance presented by the motor; at normal switching frequencies this looks pretty much like a straight line. When the current hits the upper boundary, we turn off those IGBTs, and turn on some more to reduce the current (or let the flywheel diodes do it for us – see below). When we hit the lower boundary, we switch back. Like a drunk bouncing from wall to wall in an alley, we make progress, staying within the boundaries and building the sinewave current directly. This is shown in the figure below. Clearly the trick with HCC is to know which IGBTs to turn on and off, and also to know how much current you require.

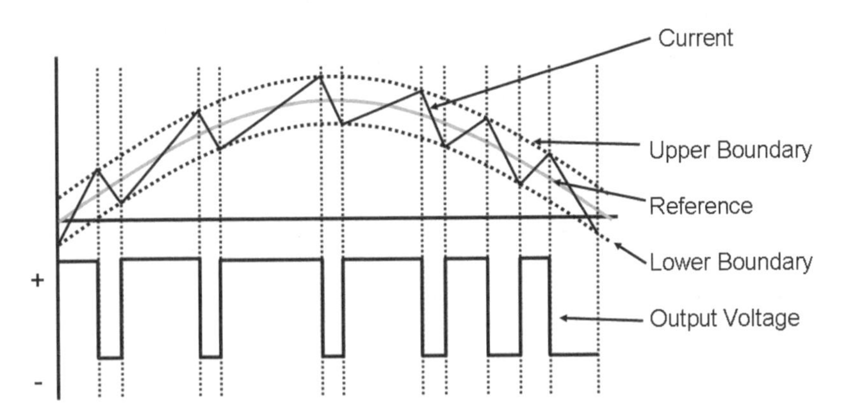

Figure 5.7 Hysteresis Current Control

Which Modulation Method is Best?

As usual, they all have their advantages. FLB minimises the switching on the IGBTs, as some are on or off for 120°, so losses are reduced. However, this leads to narrow pulses, which have their own problems; SVC avoids the narrow pulses, but the IGBTS switch all the time. HCC has the advantage that the drive is always controlling current, which gives better response sometimes. However, it switches at an uncontrolled, variable frequency that makes filter design harder, and can produce annoying audible noise. SVC is generally preferred over FLB these days, and at least one major manufacturer uses HCC.

Deadbands, Deadband Compensation and Minimum pulse widths

We mentioned above that, as IGBTs take some time to turn off, we need to allow a short 'deadband' between turning the top half of a leg off and turning the bottom on (or visa-versa). On small IGBTs (say 10A devices), turn off time can be as short as 200ns, but large devices can take a microsecond or more. A long time – in electronics at least (but not so in the real world- a supersonic aircraft travels less than a millimetre in a microsecond).

Including this deadband in the pulse pattern makes a small but significant difference to the waveform shape, so the pulse widths need to be recalculated to account for this. In the same way, removing small pulses will also make minor changes to the pattern. As deadband times, and minimum pulse widths vary with IGBT power, and switching frequency may be changed by the customer, recalculation of the pulse width can be pretty complex.

Voltage control

So far we've only talked about generating a pulse pattern in terms of producing a sinusoidally weighted pulse stream to achieve a three phase current of variable frequency in the motor. That's hard enough. But we saw in Chapter 3 that the flux in the motor is largely dependent on the applied voltage. More precisely, the flux generating current is largely dependent on the applied voltage. So we need to control the voltage as well. Again, by controlling the pulse widths, we can reduce or increase the overall voltage value while still producing a sine wave weighted output. At the same time, we can measure the DC link, and compensate for any ripple or voltage variation by (you've guess it) controlling the pulse width.

Put another way, our inverter, by modulating the pulse width only, can generate a variable voltage, variable frequency three phase AC waveform suitable for induction motor control. Pretty neat.

Currents and Commutation Diodes

We've been talking about creating modulation patterns by turning IGBTs on and off to generate sinewave currents in the motor. The actual current patterns produced are complex, as different IGBTs switch on and off within a window. However, the result is a current in each phase of the motor that has a ripple frequency dependent on the switching frequency. The figure above gives an idea of the current in an hysteresis current control drive and motor; with an FLB or SVC control, using a fixed switching frequency, the current is similar, as show in the figure below. Here, the output current lags the voltage as the load is inductive.

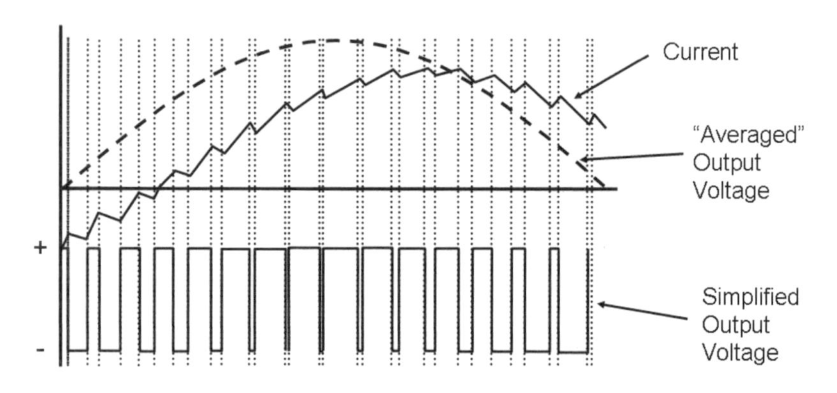

Figure 5.8 Space Vector or FLB Currents

It is important to note that the commutation diodes will always connect the motor to the DC link so as to reduce the current if the IGBTs are not actively forcing the current. Current and voltage may be in or out of phase, so an IGBT may apply a positive voltage to a negative current flow. Current chooses to flow up the flywheel diode rather than change direction – remember it's inductive. Take the example, shown in the figure below, where the U phase voltage has become negative (that is, pulses from U-IGBT are wider than from U+), but the current in the U phase of the motor is still positive. U- IGBT turns on, but the current stays positive and draws current up the diode next to it. U- goes off, U+ IGBT turns on, the current now switches to U+ IGBT and the diode blocks (this takes a little time as described in chapter 2). Notice that, on average, the current is falling, which is what you'd expect as the voltage is negative. It's a little confusing, but it sorts itself out in the end.

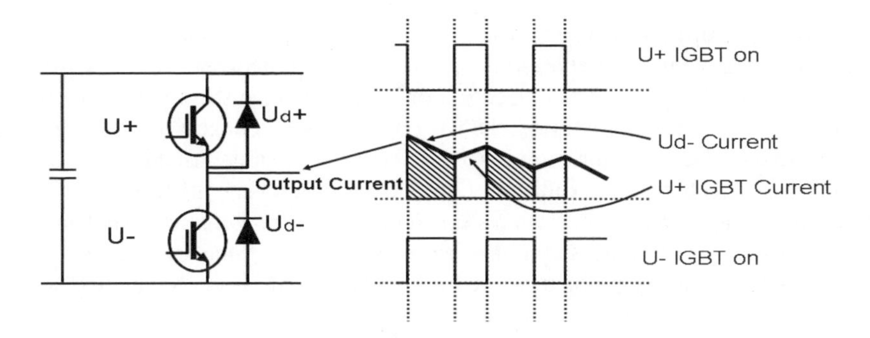

Figure 5.9 IGBT and Commutation Diode currents

Reversing and Regenerating

In chapter 3 we found that the induction motor would reverse its direction of rotation if any two supply phase connections were swapped. In a variable speed drive, this is pretty easy to do under software control. Normally of course the drive will be reversed by reducing the output frequency of the drive to zero, then reversing the phases and increasing the output frequency to the desired, reversed speed.

Regeneration is another matter. In the lift application discussed in chapter 4, the loading in the lift determines whether the lift returns energy to the motor or not, so the drive is not in control of the direction of energy flow. With a direct on-line motor, the mains voltage maintains the motor flux so generation –or motoring – can continue. The same is true with an inverter fed motor; as long as the inverter keeps switching, regeneration can take place as long as the load is supplying energy to the motor. If the inverter output is switched off, the regeneration will stop as soon as the flux collapses, usually within a few milliseconds. But what happens if we keep the drive running? The energy will return to the inverter as current out of phase with the output voltage; that is, negative power. This will be directed to the DC link in the same way that the motoring current is; that is, through a combination of IGBT currents and flywheel diode currents. Note that the flywheel diodes don't suddenly act as rectifiers.

The current arrives on the DC link, and cannot return to the supply (in a normal, simple inverter at least) because the rectifier diodes prevent this. So the current charges the DC link capacitor instead, and the DC link voltage rises. If regeneration continues, the DC link capacitor voltage will continue to rise until the capacitor explodes, the IGBTs fail, or (more usually) the inverter detects the over voltage and trips the inverter. Now the flux in the motor collapses and regeneration stops. The motor is now free wheeling and coasts to a stop, or speeds up if the load is still supplying energy. This is now someone else's problem as the load on the crane falls to ground; maybe a mechanical brake is a good idea.

However, this is not very satisfactory. Regeneration occurs in many applications, and will also occur if we want to slow down a high inertia load rapidly, which is often the case in manufacturing applications. If we fit a larger DC link capacitor we can be a little more flexible, but this costs money and space. We can't easily put the energy back to the supply, so we need to burn it off somehow.

The answer is to connect a resistor across the DC link to burn this energy. We do this using another IGBT, known as a braking chopper because it switches in and out (chops) at typically 2kHz to maintain the DC link voltage. The chopper only needs to monitor the DC link voltage and can switch in when this goes too high, and turn off again once the voltage has fallen. Some drives have braking choppers built into the drive, some manufacturers offer small braking modules as an option, which can be connected to the DC link and include the chopper IGBT and necessary control electronics.

Sometimes a small braking resistor is included with the chopper but connections will be provided for an external resistor to be fitted by the customer to suit his needs. We'll talk more about braking resistors, and their applications in chapter 9. Regeneration in this way is sometimes called dynamic or resistive braking, and can be very effective in slowing a high inertia load rapidly.

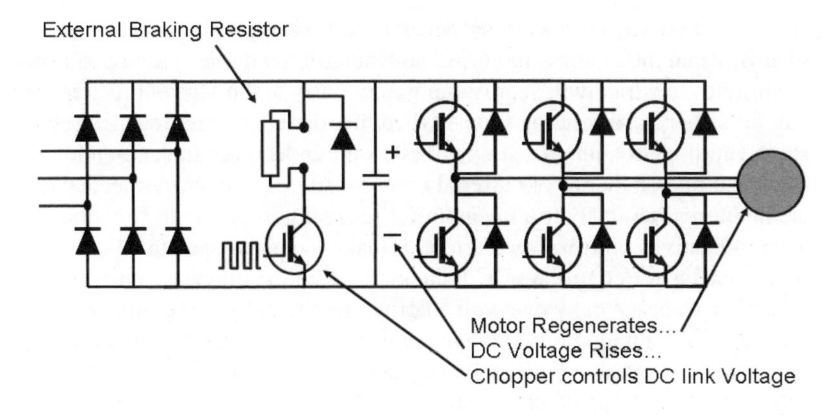

Figure 5.10 Regeneration with braking chopper

Fully Regenerative Drives

It is possible to build an AC drive that is fully regenerative; that is, it returns energy to the supply. The simplest way to do this is to fit a second inverter to the front of the drive in place of the rectifier, as shown in the figure below.

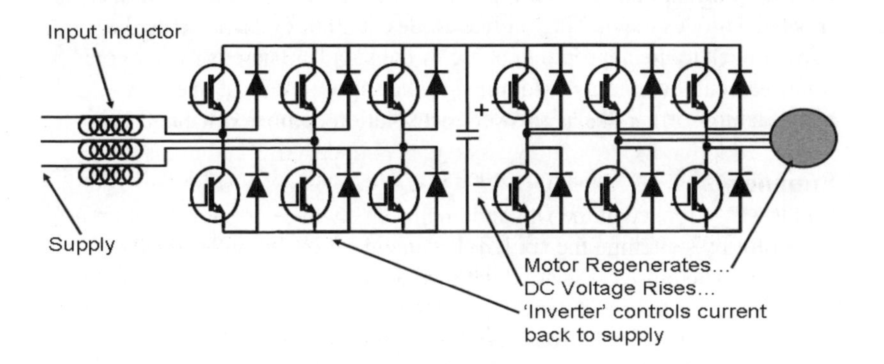

Figure 5.11 Regenerative Drive

We've already seen that an inverter can supply energy in both directions (that is, when the motor is motoring or generating), so a second inverter on the front of the drive will supply energy normally to the 'drive' inverter, and will pass energy back to the supply when the 'drive' inverter regenerates. However, it's not quite that simple. Just as the inductance in the motor limits the rate of change of current in the inverter, an inductor is needed on the input inverter to control the input (or regenerative) current. Now that we have full active control of the current, it makes sense to operate this inverter so that we have a controlled DC link, and take a nice sine wave current (as opposed to a nasty spiky one with a normal rectifier) from the supply. We'll see that this is a major advantage in controlling harmonics in chapter 10. This type of sine wave input, fully regenerative drive has various names, depending on the manufacturer, such as "Active Front End", or AFE. It is, of course, an expensive solution, and really beyond the scope of this book, although with the ever falling costs of control, and the rising cost of energy, it may become more popular.

A halfway solution is also possible, where IGBTs are also used at the front of the drive as well as the back, but do not act like an inverter. In this arrangement the diodes act as rectifier diodes, supplying energy from the mains as normal during motoring, but during regeneration the IGBTs act as 'reversed diodes', switching on like diodes at 50 or 60 Hz to route the current back to the appropriate phase of the supply. There is no harmonic improvement, but energy is returned to the supply. At least one manufacturer offers this as a lower cost solution compared with AFE.

Summary

So far we've looked at the way in which a sine wave current is built up in the motor by switching the six IGBTs on and off in a complex modulation sequence. The pulses are varied in pulse width not only to produce a sinusoidal modulation pattern (to produce the required sinusoidal current) but also to vary the effective overall voltage to give the correct flux generating current in the motor. The frequency of the output current determines the motor speed (less any slip) while the switching frequency is chosen as a compromise between switching losses, current ripple, audible noise etc.

Different modulation patterns may be used to produce the necessary output; these are further adapted to account for deadbands and removal of short pulses. Commutation diodes play a key role in maintaining the current.

Reversing can be easily handled by reversing the phase sequence, but regeneration requires a braking chopper or, for a fully regenerative system, more IGBTs and control for the rectifier.

We now need to look at the components and controls needed to generate these pulses, and how to assemble them into a practical drive.

6. Drive Control and Protection Systems

We've now looked at how the power part of a DC and AC drive works, so we have a pretty good idea of the control circuits that are needed. In the next two chapters we'll examine the control requirements for drives, starting with the customer interface – the inputs and outputs used to start and stop the drive. So much electronics comes down to 'it's a microprocessor with some interface' that we'll look at some of the circuits used in older drives, rather than try to discuss how the firmware in the central controller works.
The key features of a typical drive controller are shown in the figure below. The Central Processing Unit (the CPU) is clearly handling all the functions, but there are many interface circuits between it and the real world. Let's look at these.

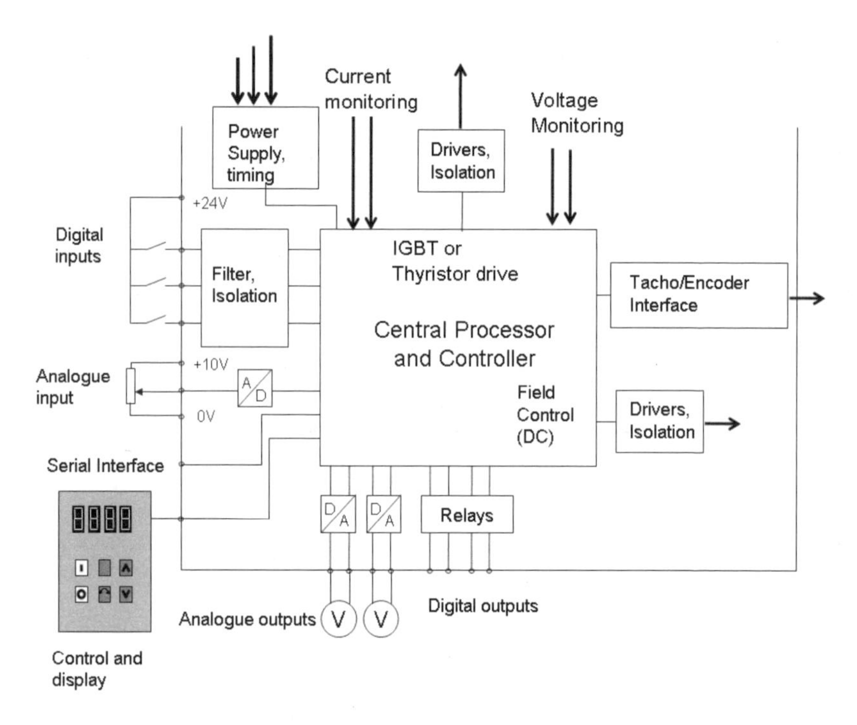

Figure 6.1 AC or DC Drive – Block diagram Control

Power Supply

Of course the controller needs a power supply, so a simple switched mode power supply (SMPS) is used to provide several different supplies, some of which may be isolated for use by digital inputs (see below). Actually the SMPS is not so simple as it sounds, running from an industrial mains, which may be as high as 500V AC, rectifying to DC above 700V, generating 1400V if a flyback converter is used. The basic principles of a flyback converter were described in chapter 2, and the power supply for an AC drive, which is a bit more complicated, is described in chapter 7. Remember many parts of the drive, including the power supply are at very high voltage. Fingers off!

Inputs and Outputs

Serial Interface

Many drives are now controlled via a serial interface, and a serial interface is indeed usually provided. If nothing else, it makes testing and calibration of drives easier. Most manufacturers have their own proprietary protocol, and there are several open systems (see chapter 8), but nearly all use the RS 485 hardware specification. See box: **RS485**.

RS 485

RS 485 is a fully differential interface, which ensures that it is pretty noise immune. This is important, as noise and interference can take its toll, especially if the interface is dragged around a plant whose grounding is somewhat suspect (see chapter 10). The serial interface connection will be filtered and buffered as much as possible before connecting to the CPU.
It is also designed for multidrop, unlike Ethernet, which uses point to point connection using a router or switch for each node. With RS485 you can add as many nodes as you want just by paralleling the connections. Of course, this depends a little on cable length and driver capability, and a lot on the protocol that you're using – how many addresses that are allowed etc. In practice, a simple protocol may permit (say) 31 nodes, Profibus for example, which is a more complex system, can have 126. A node can consist of a drive, PC, industrial controller, or anything else with suitable software and RS485 drivers.

Without extra buffering, RS485 can drive cable up to 1000m, or so the specification says. In practice, for reasonable baud rates, a couple of hundred metres would be OK. Baud rates in industry tend to be pretty slow compared with Ethernet, 10 or 12Mbaud being considered fast.
The figure below shows how the drivers in a RS485 system are arranged. All the electronics are protected against short circuit, voltage transients (up to 60V) etc, but rely on the software protocol to prevent message collisions. Needless to say, all the bits are built into a chip that costs a few pence, although the protection circuitry (see later), added from bitter experience, is external. Incidentally, a serial comms line is a classic transmission line, and should always be terminated with a suitable matching resistor at the end nodes to prevent reflections (check the handbook on this). Biasing resistors are also included; often these are built into products and can be switched in. The different protocols are described briefly in chapter 8.

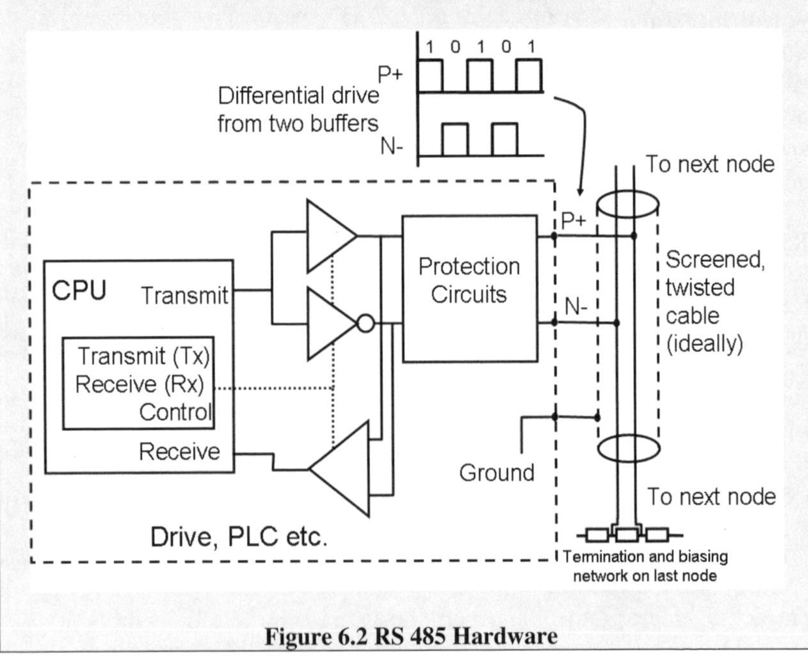

Figure 6.2 RS 485 Hardware

Digital inputs

For many users digital inputs are still the preferred way to switch the drive on and off. These inputs may be connected to switches and buttons on a cabinet or control desk, or directly to a PLC. (What's a PLC? A Programmable Logic Controller is a modular computer widely used in industry for all kinds of control and monitoring) Many digital inputs use optocouplers to give galvanic isolation (from the control board 0V), greatly reducing interference problems. Often an isolated power supply is dedicated for their use. The digital inputs usually have a lot of protection components associated with them, such as resistors to limit the input current, diodes to the 0V and supply to limit voltage, and capacitors to ground to divert high frequency noise.

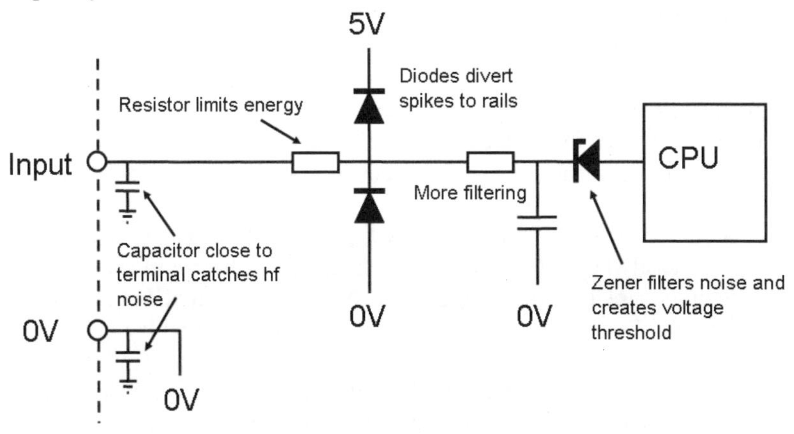

Figure 6.3 Input Protection

The software in the CPU takes care of any noise still present by de-bouncing the signals; typically the signal has to be present for several milliseconds to be considered valid, but this delay can be removed by the customer if fast response is needed.

Most digital inputs are programmable; that is, pre-assigned functions such as run/stop or reverse can be changed to suit the needs of an installation. Functions such as run left, run right, Jog (or 'inch' in US), fixed speed select, reset fault etc. are commonly provided. More sophisticated controls such as local (front panel) or remote (serial interface) command select are also available. The power of software limits the possibilities only to the imagination of the engineer and the number of bugs he has already introduced.

Digital inputs usually need a minimum of five or six volts to be regarded as high; up to 30V or more being permitted. The sense of some digital inputs can be inverted, so they must be pulled low to be active; this suits some oriental PLCs, which for some reason work in the opposite sense to the normal 'Active high'.

Digital Outputs

Or relays as we like to call them. It may seem a little old fashioned, but relays are still the ideal solution for indications such as 'running' 'tripped' 'current limit' etc. (you've guessed it – these functions are also programmable). Relays are fully isolated, can switch mains contactors or lamps, can easily be tested and are reasonably cheap. Some drives will provide optocouplers here, or even open collector transistors, but relays are more flexible. Connected to a plant supervisory system or a big red light, they'll indicate drive status without problems. If a relay is programmed to indicate a fault condition, then it will usually be energised when the fault is not present. Then you'll get a fault indication if the wire breaks, but you'll have to mask the fault in your supervisory system when the drive is powered off as the relay de-energises - more work for the software automation engineers. Some relays are not mains rated; read the handbook. Sometimes the limiting factor is the connection terminals on the control board, which may be small and not mains rated – it's still a limitation though.

Analog Input
Again, speed demand (or torque in some cases) may come from a PLC or via the serial interface, but it's also still common to connect a potentiometer (pot) to the drive to set the speed. Isolation could be expensive here, so the signal is usually just fed to an A to D converter, often built into the CPU. See box: **A to D and D to A Converters**. 10 bit accuracy is a minimum requirement really; not so much for the absolute accuracy, but for the resolution. You don't want the motor to change speed in noticeable steps as you turn the pot slowly.

If a pot is connected we'll need a 0V and a precision, low drift (usually 10V) reference. Calibration of this during manufacture (rather than using a high cost pre-calibrated reference) reduces the cost. Some drives have more than one analogue input. This is useful if you want to connect a sensor to monitor or control temperature, pressure flow rate or whatever. This feedback signal can then be used in a closed loop control system, described later.

Most inputs can be programmed or adjusted with DIP switches (that is, tiny PCB mounted switches that can only be operated by an elf) to accept 0 – 20mA or 4 – 20mA signals instead of 0 – 10V. Current loops like this tend to be more noise immune due to their low impedance, so they are often used for connections from PLCs or other controllers.

Analogue Outputs
Speed and current meters on the front of the cabinet look nice, and an analogue output or two can drive these, or can be connected to other monitoring systems. Needless to say, the analogue outputs can often be programmed and scaled to indicate anything you may wish to know – heatsink temperature for example, although speed and current seem to be pretty popular. Again, several outputs may be provided and isolation is unlikely, and options of 0 – 20mA or 4 – 20mA signals instead of 0 – 10V possible. If you use the analogue output to indicate torque or output frequency, you can connect it to another drive, and that drive will track the first, matching frequency or sharing torque. Not quite that simple, but it works.

A to D and D to A Converters

Good A to D and D to A converters used to be expensive and whole companies made a living out of supplying high tech solutions for us. Nowadays we have a CPU with all the functions we need built in; we may even choose to design our own A to D and include it in circuitry on the DC link (see chapter 7).
Most built in CPU A to Ds are of the successive approximation type, where the input signal is compared with the output of a fast, accurate internal D to A converter. The way this works is that the D to A is initially set to 0, and then each bit is set to 1 in turn, starting with the most significant. The output of the D to A is compared to the input signal each time, and if the D to A output is higher than the input signal then that bit is reset to 0. In this way the D to A ends up with a code representing a voltage less than the input but closer than 1 least significant bit – which was the aim of the exercise in the first place.
Another approach is to use sigma delta conversion, which sounds quite impressive, but is basically a voltage controlled oscillator, with some feedback. As usual, there is an integrator with a reset, which creates a pulse, the pulse feeds a counter, and also resets the integrator. The greater the input voltage, the faster the integration takes place, so the more pulses are generated. The trick now is to feedback the signal (the pulse stream) to the input, subtracting the pulses from the input signal, so the difference (the delta) drives the integrator. This closed loop approach makes for a highly accurate and fast A to D conversion, the pulse stream being fed to the CPU to determine the analogue input value.
Most microprocessors have several channels of A to D built in, often using an analogue switch so that one A to D can measure all the channels to save cost.
D to A converters of the type needed to drive analogue outputs are a bit easier. Set up a timer in the CPU, and use this to generate a pulse whose width is proportional to the digital value. Output this via a buffer and reference (so the pulse height is constant), repeat at a sensible clock rate, and stick it through a simple filter; you'll have a voltage proportional to the original digital value.

The outputs and inputs of the drive, together with 0V, +24V etc. are brought out to a strip of terminals for the customer to connect to. If they seem a little small, it is because the designer has to keep the overall size of the drive, and the control board to a minimum. If they seem to be arranged at random, it will be to optimise the pcb layout to reduce EMC (see chapter 10) rather than confuse the wireman.

Control and Display

Most drives have some form of control and display panel, if only for programming. The display may consist of a seven segment LED display or a simple LCD panel. The LCD panel usually has more information, but in a dark cubicle in a dirty factory seven segment LEDs come into their own. Membrane push buttons allow starting, stopping and programming, with speed up and slow down buttons usually included. When commissioning it's always good to be able to run the drive from this panel independent of any control system. The panel is usually connected to the control board by a multiway cable or serial link, and, if the designer has thought about it, may often be detached and mounted on the cubicle door using a short extension cable.

Figure 6.4 Typical Drive Control and Display Panel

Sometimes, the standard control panel is pretty basic, but fancy panels may be bought (at a price) which may control more than one drive over a serial interface, offer text in different languages, enhanced diagnostics and the ability to mount on a cubicle door. The control and display panel and the terminals are all connected to the CPU.

Detachable control panels may be able to copy (upload) programming information from a drive, and when connected to another drive, download the settings. This is sometimes called cloning, and can be very useful for machine builders who want the same settings in every machine.

Central Processor Unit

There must be very few pieces of electronics, let alone industrial electronics, which don't have microprocessor and associated memory. The advantages are clear, with easy handling of serial interfaces, D to A and A to D conversion, displays etc. It also permits all the analogue functions of the past to be digitised. There is nothing special about the CPUs used in drives; they have a processor, memory, serial ports, real time clocks etc. The firmware (the fixed control programme) is probably developed using C or C++ or some derivative, complied and, when the software is finally deemed ready for release, either a ROM mask version of the CPU containing the firmware (see below) is ordered for production, and everyone hopes they got it right, or FLASH memory is used with the possibility to reprogram drives later to eliminate any bugs that have crept in.

Programming the CPU

On early drives, an acceleration rate, maximum frequency, current limit etc. not to mention any factory calibration, would be adjusted using preset potentiometers. Now this is all programmable, and to make it simple (or complicated) for the user, these variables are usually set by setting parameters. For example, parameter number 99 – maybe shown in the display as P099 (you can do a 'P' in a seven segment display), may set the current limit. For a user to set this up, he presses P (or maybe 'Prog') on the control and display panel, and maybe P001 is displayed. Then he scrolls through the parameters on the display (using up and down buttons) until 099 is reached, presses P again to view the present value (say 25 Amps), changes the value as required with up and down keys, and exits programming mode. He does this for his acceleration rates, digital input functions, serial communications settings etc. Easy! Additional, hidden parameters can contain calibration information or other data set by the manufacturer. There is also usually a block of hidden parameters that contain information relating to the power rating of the drive. Usually the firmware is common to all sizes of drive, so the CPU is told during test it is controlling a 37kW drive, not a 370kW – useful to know when you want to limit the current.

For the user, there may also be read only parameters that provide information like output current, heatsink temperature etc. Unfortunately, all this leads to a large list of parameters, which may or may not be logically arranged, as of course their numbers have grown with every software release.

We'll talk more about the different functions and features and why you need to adjust them in chapter 8. Some drives come with hundreds of parameters, so if you want to set up a complex control system this can take ages (especially when trying to read a badly copied parameter list on top of a sugar crusher). So most drives come with a simple PC programming tool that connects over the serial link. Now you have to balance your laptop on top of the sugar crusher, but at least you can read the screen. Of course you can upload and download complete parameter sets as well, saving programming time for similar drive applications. Alternatively, if you have a simple application maybe you only need to change one or two parameters. This makes life a lot easier!

CPU Hardware – Memory

A drive CPU contains several different sorts of memory, and its worth explaining them and their different functions. Most types of memory are now available on the microprocessor chip, and a large user like a drive manufacturer can mix and match memory – at a price – to suit their needs.

ROM. Read Only Memory

ROM is the lowest cost memory in quantity, and the firmware is fixed when the chip is made. If you are making lots of drives, you want to get your firmware – your operating system – onto ROM as soon as possible. If, subsequently, too many bugs are found, you'll need to scrap your chips, and explain to someone very high up what went wrong. Going to ROM is a tough call, but at least ROM can't get corrupted or changed by the customer.

RAM Random Access Memory

Fast memory used by the processor as working memory. PCs have vast amounts of this, but an embedded CPU only needs a few kilobytes. RAM is volatile; that is, the memory is lost at power down.

Flash Memory

Flash is used to retain data; that is, it is non volatile. It has two main uses in a drive. It is used to retain customer settings during power down – the user doesn't want to re-programme his drive every shift.

Flash is also used if the development guys are a bit cowardly and want to remain flexible with the firmware rather than go to ROM. ROM is cheaper, but we've seen if you get ROM wrong it's embarrassing. A reasonable compromise is to use Flash for the first few thousand, and then go to ROM, although these days IC manufacturers find that it is more cost effective to sell one type of controller fitted with Flash memory rather than several variants with different ROM masks for different customers. For specialist drives which need flexibility, Flash is normally used as the customer is paying a lot in any case.

Incidentally, if you are continually changing parameters over a serial link, then you can choose to use RAM to store the values instead of Flash, because Flash has a limited number of read/write cycles; maybe 10,000 or 100,000, but limited nevertheless. If you write a new speed value every couple of seconds you can hit this limit quite soon.

CPU Hardware – The Processor

Not much to say here. A microprocessor is a microprocessor. Early drives had rudimentary 'control and supervisory' processors that just took over the handling of inputs and outputs, serial communications etc. The software was minimal, and any cheap micro would do the job. Now with the hundreds of parameters available, and complex control calculations needed for fancy control systems, drive design engineers demand the fastest, best micro they can afford. If this speed and power leads to 'bloatware' in the firmware, full of bugs and difficult to maintain, that's a problem for drive development managers. I digress.

What does the CPU actually do?

As mentioned above, a modern CPU does all the hard work of the drive. Let's look at the 'housekeeping' jobs first, and then focus on the actual control of the drive.

The CPU will probably operate on a 'timeslice' principle. Depending on the speed of the processor, it will cycle through some high priority tasks say every millisecond, some lesser priority tasks every two milliseconds, some low priority tasks every four etc. Clearly there's no point in updating the display less than every thirty two milliseconds, but the current monitor should be read as often as possible. Juggling these priorities occupies a lot of software engineers time, so lets just list typical housekeeping tasks in no particular order:

Handling Inputs:

    Digital inputs
    Analogue inputs
    Control Panel buttons
    Serial Interface

Handling outputs:

    Digital outputs (Relays)
    Analogue outputs
    Serial Interface
    Display

Miscellaneous background stuff

    Real time clock (maybe)
    Temperature monitoring or calculating
    Power calculations
    Alarm and fault handling
    Protection
    Interpreting and loading Parameter changes.
    Updating parameter values such as current
    Closed loop control (see later)

Clearly some of these are less background than others; for example, response to digital and analogue inputs must be fast in high speed control systems. These are pretty general control and monitor functions you'd find in lots of equipment, so let's look at the specific control of the drive.

CPU Drive Control Functions

The purpose of the drive is to control the speed or torque of the motor based on the demands and settings from the user, while protecting itself, and the motor, from damage. Assuming the drive has been properly installed and set up, it will wait patiently for a run command to arrive (either via a digital input, control panel or serial interface) and the housekeeping software will spot this, interpret it and things will start to happen. If everything is OK, if there is demand, (see below) the drive will produce some gate pulses to turn on the thyristors (on a DC drive) or drive the IGBTs (on an AC drive) and generate some output. We'll look in chapter 8 more closely at acceleration times, but for now, assume we accelerate the motor and load it in a civilised way.

As soon as the motor is started, the current will be monitored both to protect the motor and the drive. The current measurement is also used to calculate the torque that the motor is producing. For a DC drive this is pretty straightforward, as the armature and field currents are separate, but for an AC drive we have to separate these components; more of this later. Torque control and limiting can be pretty useful in some applications such as winding (cables, yarn, cloth etc.), or load sharing between different drives. The CPU will also monitor the DC link voltage on an AC drive; we'll see later that this rises rapidly if the motor regenerates energy back to the drive. Also, if we are trying to get very accurate speed or torque control we'll need a pretty sophisticated CPU in order to model the motor and load system. We'll see later what this means for an AC drive in particular.

We've discussed the sort of functions that a drive needs to look after itself, and to monitor inputs and control outputs, but in real applications we are also interested in the effect the drive is having on the process, and vice versa. Maybe we are monitoring speed (with an encoder) or torque of the motor, or, more likely, we are monitoring some characteristic of the process such as pressure, speed of bottles, temperature etc. So a key function of a drive is to monitor and control these, and drives use closed loop controllers to do this. We'll look at this function in some detail, as closed loop controllers are also used to control torque, speed, current and voltage (during regeneration) in many drive applications.

Closed and Open Loop Control

Industry is full of processes where we need to control something like temperature, pressure, flow rate, conveyer speed etc. Let's look at something simple, like a coolant pump, which has a variable speed drive connected to its motor. The easy thing to do is to set the pump at a speed that seems to deliver the right amount of cooling, and forget about it. This is an open loop system, and clearly won't work if the temperature changes or the fluid gets hot or whatever. A better solution is that someone checks it occasionally, and adjusts the pump accordingly. Even better is a temperature monitoring system feeds a signal back to some form of controller and the speed is continually adjusted to maintain constant temperature. This is a proper closed loop control system, so called because the feedback from the temperature sensor 'closes the loop' when it connects back to the controller.

A closed loop control system will also take account of variables such as supply voltage changes, worn pumps, etc. The world is full of closed loop systems; thermostats, cruise controllers, 'straight and level' flight control systems etc.

Note that, in this example, speed or torque are not relevant to the user. He's only interested in temperature control. But if the drive is set up correctly it can monitor a temperature sensor and adjust its speed accordingly, keeping the temperature constant and the user happy. This is a true local closed loop system.
On the other hand, drives are often part of large systems and are controlled by a central PLC or supervisory system. Now the PLC will monitor the temperature (and lots of other things) and do the hard work of the closed loop calculations (see below). The drive dumbly speeds up or slows down, commanded by the PLC. The drive is open loop, but the system is closed loop.

So far we've talked about closed loop control for external processes, controlling things like temperature, pressure, flow rate etc. However, many drives – particularly DC drives - are also involved in localised control processes, where the speed and torque of the motor are critical. We also need closed loop control if we wish to control current or torque within the drive. So a drive needs closed loop controllers internally, as well as for external control. They are also used to protect our drive and motor from over speed or over current. So let's look at open and closed loop control systems in a typical drive.

An Open Loop Control

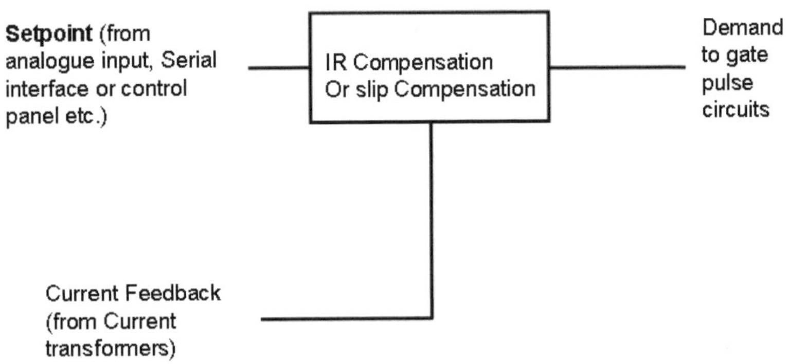

Figure 6.5 Simple Open Loop Control

The open loop control is pretty trivial, with the required speed coming from any number of sources; the required value is known as the *setpoint*. The setpoint is tweaked a little with a bit of compensation (IR comp on a DC drive, slip comp on an AC drive – see chapters 4 and 8) to improve the open loop speed holding; otherwise the signal goes pretty much straight to the control circuits as the raw speed demand. Fine if this is part of a larger process that is continually adjusting the setpoint.

A Simple Speed Control Closed Loop

The basis of a simple speed controller is shown in the figure below. Here we are concerned with maintaining constant motor speed, but the same principles apply when controlling pressure or flow, as we'll see later.

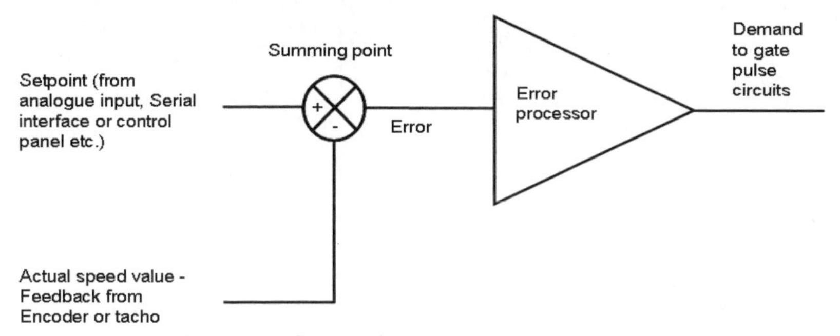

Figure 6.6 Simple Closed Loop Speed Control

The setpoint comes from the user or his automation system as before. The actual – measured or monitored – value in this case is coming from an encoder or tacho. The setpoint and actual value need to be scaled pretty much the same; if they aren't there can be lots of problems setting things up.

The key to any closed loop is the summing point. Actually, the signals are subtracted at the summing point, and an error signal generated. Clearly the greater the error at this point the more we need to adjust our speed to get the setpoint and actual values about the same. This error signal is processed mathematically (we'll see why and how) and the resulting signal is our demand that sets the motor speed by voltage control on a DC drive or frequency control on an AC drive. Easy. The closed loop, or servo, system works continuously adjusting the demand to keep the error at a minimum. We'll use the word servo quite a bit to describe a closed loop controller – it's not strictly accurate, but everyone uses it.
Speed control systems with encoders are used widely on DC drives, which tend to be used now on precision applications, but not so much on simpler AC drives.

Torque Control

The Torque control – or current limit – controller looks virtually the same.

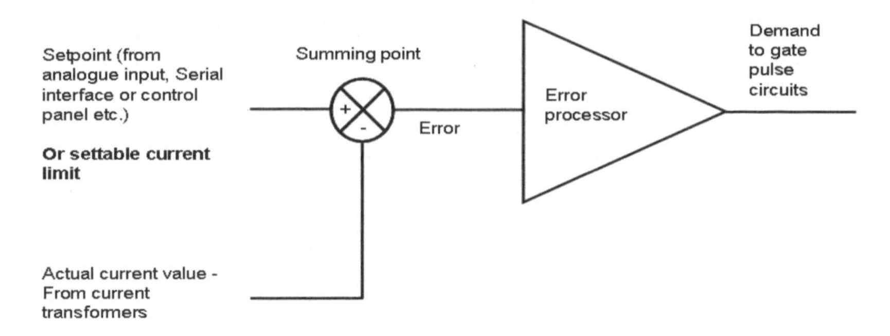

Figure 6.7 Simple Closed Loop Torque or Current Control

If you're controlling torque, this is your setpoint that you are interested in. If you are just setting a current limit for motor or drive protection, you'll just set a parameter (or adjust a preset pot on an old drive) and forget about it.

You may not even be aware of the current servo, leaving it at its default setting protecting the drive (see later). But the closed loop system is there, with summing point and error processor in case you need it.

Speed and Torque Control

So we have two closed loop controllers. However, you can only choose to control one of these at any one time. Say we control the speed. The speed control closed loop works away, continuously adjusting the frequency output of the drive respectively to keep the speed at the desired level. The load is normal, so the drive doesn't current limit or anything. Now suppose the load increases abnormally as a tree branch (or laptop) falls into the sugar crusher. The torque rises, the current rises, and the current servo, dormant until now, suddenly decides the drive has had enough and takes over from the speed servo, rapidly reducing the speed in order to reduce the current. Now the current controller is dominant, and the speed loop inactive (actually demanding more speed, but being ignored) until the overload clears. Then the current control backs off, and speed control resumes; we'll see later how this changeover occurs.

Now consider an application where the user is using the current servo as a torque controller, controlling tension in a line making paper. Maybe we are maintaining constant tension (using some rollers) on the paper as it is dried or glazed. With fixed diameter rollers, tension is torque, which is handy. So we run in constant torque, the current servo doing its job. Suddenly the paper snaps. No joke on a line running at ten metres per second or more. The drive speeds up the rollers, trying to maintain constant tension, but with no load on them they just go faster and faster. Paper is going everywhere. Luckily, the speed servo wakes up, and limits the speed to a safe level; probably the supervisory system will shut the line down shortly afterwards. In both cases, we are working with one servo, and the other is a back up. How do we switch between the two?
In analogue terms there are two easy ways to do it. Parallel or series servos. The parallel servo is easier to understand, providing we are prepared to think a bit negative; in the figure below, the servo with the *lowest* voltage is in control. Just check through that. Imagine all the diodes in the diagram are disconnected. Now the meeting point of the diodes is pulled high by the resistor, which represents high demand to the drive output, speeding up the drive.

So to take control, (with the diodes reconnected) any one of the servos, or even the switch at the bottom, has to pull the meeting point of the diodes low. In practice, one of these is always doing so. Let's see how this happens.

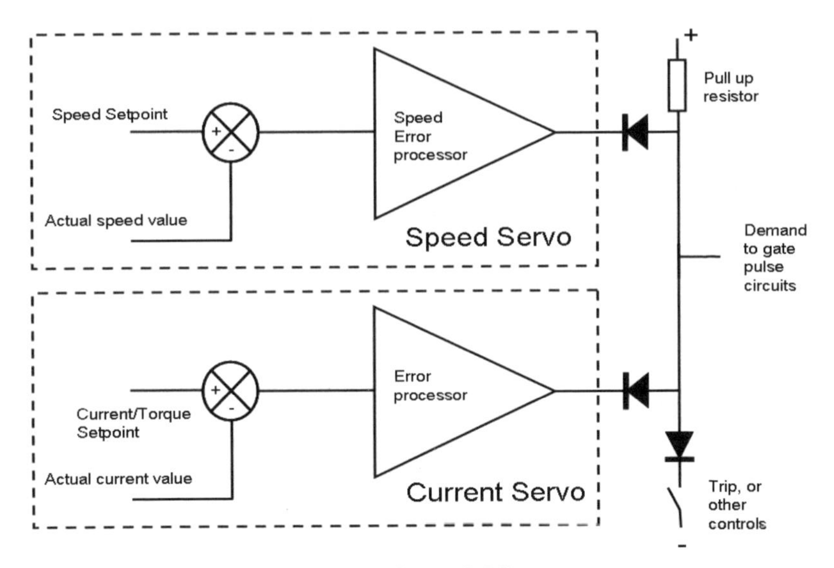

Figure 6.8 Parallel Servos

Now, back to our sugar crusher, running nicely in speed control. The speed control servo is in control, making a demand and therefore a low voltage at the output of the error processor. The current is low, so the output of the current servo error processor is high. The diodes on the error processor's output stop any mixing at this point by playing 'lowest one wins'. The output of the speed servo is lower than the current servo, so its diode is forward biased and connects it to the demand. That is, the speed servo is doing everything, the current servo nothing.

Now comes your current overload (the tree branch or your laptop in the crusher). The current rises, the error increases, the current error servo output falls, and if it gets lower than the speed error processor, it takes over (that is, the speed servo diode blocks, the current servo diode conducts), and you're running in current limit. Simple. When the load goes away, the diodes automatically switch back. The diodes are automatically switching between servos – lowest one takes control.

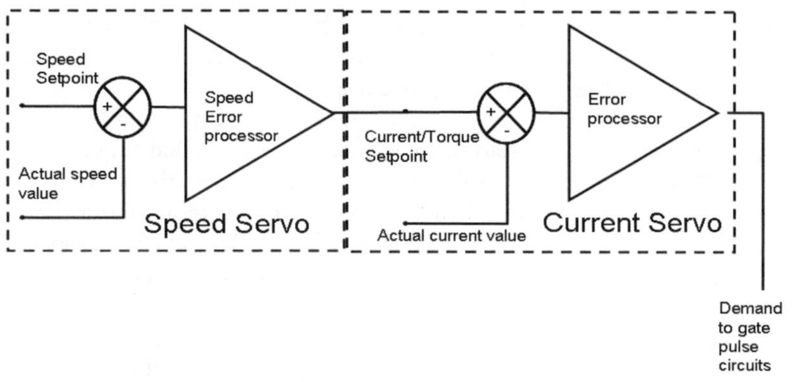

Figure 6.9 Series Servos

Guess what? In this arrangement, the servos are in series. Now the speed servo feeds the output of its error processor to the setpoint of the current/torque servo. This is a bit harder to understand. Think of the drive running in current limit all the time, but with the speed servo constantly adjusting that current limit setpoint to get the speed it wants. Of course you may reach the point where the speed is limited because the current limit servo thinks there's too much current, and reduces the output irrespective of what the speed servo is demanding – current limit again.

We won't go into the merits of series and parallel servos, but briefly, you can see that a series servo has the advantage that the current limit is always active and therefore faster. However, the error processors can interact on a series system, making it difficult to analyse and stabilise, as we'll see in a moment. Setting up a parallel servo can therefore be easier; you can also tag more servos or controls on by adding more diodes, like a trip signal that pulls demand low instantly.

Of course, with a CPU, all this is handled in the software, which is usually more like a series servo.

Stabilising Closed Loop Controllers

So we have our two (or maybe more) servo systems, one of which is trying to respond to setpoint demands and/or, changes in the load, supply voltage etc. In order to have fast and accurate response, we need to amplify the error signal that is driving our demand. However, if we have a high gain here, you can easily imagine how the system can become unstable.

So we need as high a gain as possible, but with some form of filtering –not too much or the system response will be slow. We could also look at the rate of change of the actual value, to improve response here.

Sounds easy, but this is the start of control theory, and you don't want to get into that. What we have to do is to tune the response of the drive servo to suit the system. Conventional control theory says, if you know all the losses, inertias, loads etc. in a system you can simulate and calculate your response. In practice this is very difficult. (but in some cases necessary. You can't tune the space shuttle's controls during first launch)
Most control systems are therefore tuned and set up during commissioning, fortunately by experienced engineers who can avoid breaking things. Fortunately as well, most systems can be tuned by adjusting three key parameters:

Proportional Gain
Multiply the error by a constant, the gain. The higher the gain, the more responsive, but potentially unstable the system is.

Integral term
The integral term acts as a filter, slowing any changes in error. This tends to damp down the system.

Differential term
This is really the opposite of the integral term, exaggerating any changes in the error. Actually in many applications you don't need this.

Proportional, Integral and Differential have become buzzwords in control theory, and closed loop control systems are often referred to as PID systems. One of the problems here is that these terms interact, and adjusting one usually requires changes to the others. The figure below shows how, in an old fashioned servo, the PID terms were controlled by operational amplifiers and a few passive components and some preset pots. These circuits are the core of the error processor blocks we saw in the servo systems described earlier.

Incidentally, this means if you have any significant gain in your error processors, they will sit at the end stop (i.e. the positive supply) when dormant, and will literally slew into action when needed.

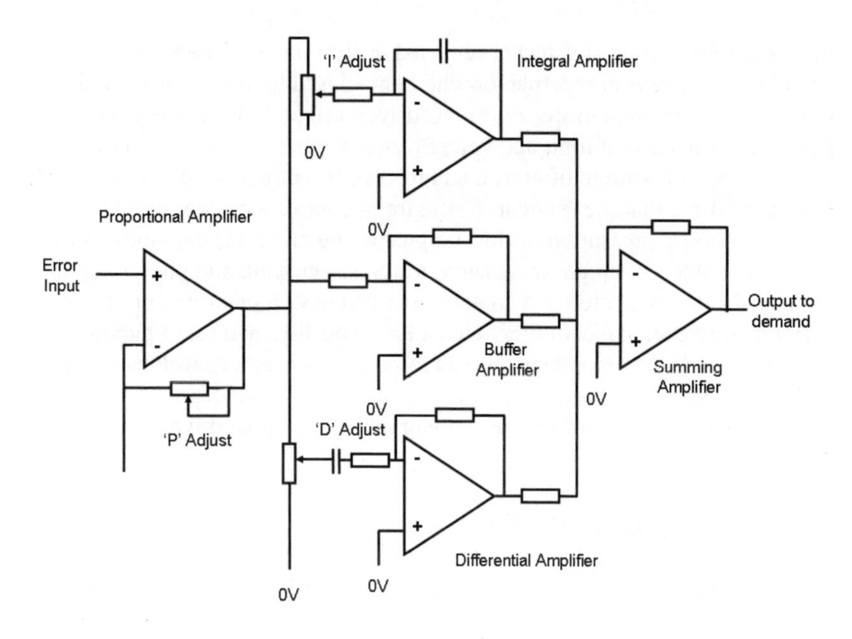

Figure 6.10 Error Processing

Nowadays, the CPU and firmware handle all these servos and control loops, but the principles are the same, you are just adjusting parameter values instead of preset pots. How to tune and adjust a servo system is beyond the scope of this book. Let's just say carefully and with experience. Incorrect scaling of the signals, noise on signals etc, often cause a lot of problems in control loops; and it's always worth checking these first, for instance by checking the feedback signal is within the range you expect, and not too noisy.

Closed Loop Control External to the Drive

A speed controller with torque or current limiting is a pretty common application for a DC drive, where precision control is an advantage. So these closed loop systems are pretty standard on DC drives, and on more sophisticated AC drives.

In recent years, AC drives have been used in simpler applications where open loop control is acceptable, or where the closed loop work is done by PLCs or other automation systems. AC drives still include servo systems for torque control, current limit and voltage control during regeneration. It's quite easy in software to offer as a feature an extra closed loop controller within the drive that the user can configure to control whatever he wants. So he can connect a pressure transducer signal to the drive, programme this as the actual value, set up the spare servo to read a setpoint, and (assuming the drive and motor are fitted to a compressor) you have a pressure controller without any external electronics. This means you'll have a set of parameters to control the PID components of the closed loop system, as well as scaling for the feedback.
Closed loop control figures in one way or another in most drive applications.

Drive and Motor Protection

It's pretty important to protect the drive and motor, so let's see how that's done.

Protection – Overload

We can damage a motor or a drive pretty quickly if we have too much current for any significant amount of time. However, we want to get the best from the motor, and all motors will run in overload for a short time (see chapter 3), so we need a little intelligence. If we are very clever, we'll have some form of software model of the thermal capacity of the motor and drive, and how the current heats it up. Now we can use the model to calculate the temperature of the motor, drive, and even parts of the drive like the thyristors or IGBTs. As we go into overload, we monitor this modelled temperature and if things get too hot, we'll raise an alarm and, if necessary, slow down to reduce load, or trip. Of course, this relies on having good models and knowing the effect of high current and maybe other losses on the motor and drive. Actually it works quite well, providing the user has told (i.e. programmed) the drive with information about the motor. A 30kW drive with a 15kW motor will allow 30kW or more of load unless it knows better. Also, if the motor has a shaft mounted fan, rather than a separate cooling fan, this will affect load capability at low speed as the cooling will be a lot less. Again, the modelling and software can account for this as it knows the motor speed, current and the cooling effect of the fan.

Without this modelling you can still get good performance by making some crude assumptions about the capability of the drive and motor. Or at least you can make a specification to the drives designer to allow loading of, say, 150% for 60 seconds. With this sort of permitted overload we can tolerate some shock loads (when the laptop falls into the crusher) or short term overloads as we run up. This makes the drive more useable, and means you don't need to select a larger drive to handle occasional overloads. Hence a drive may have several different, programmable current limits for different times, or have thermal modelling programmes that are based on information about the motor and drive, and adapt the current limit as needed. Or it may have a combination of both; this makes set up complicated if you want to get the most out your motor and drive.

Short circuits and seized motors are something else. The current will rise rapidly if the motor is stopped or stalled (see chapter 3). Most drives will detect this and trip the drive immediately; but bear in mind we can turn a thyristor on, but can't turn it off like an IGBT in an AC drive. Just as well we can fuse them then.

In summary, we'll end up with some sort of overload capability as shown in the figure below. In this case three different current limits may be set giving a good performance envelope, but staying within the capabilities of the motor and drive.

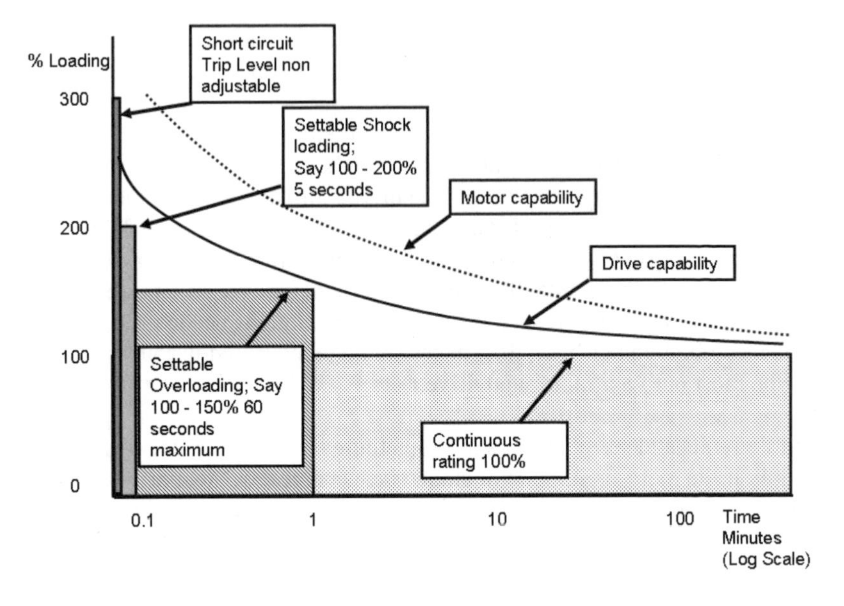

Figure 6.11 Overload Capability and Settings

All this depends on our assumptions about the thermal models. What happens if a cooling fan fails, or a filter gets blocked, or the cabinet gets too hot due to poor design?

Protection – Overheating

We mentioned before that the thyristors get hot as they carry current and are usually fitted onto a heatsink. Very large drives have water-cooled heatsinks, but most drives are air cooled, usually fan assisted. The heatsink is probably fitted with a temperature sensor, which may be a simple thermal switch, or more likely, a PTC, a Positive Temperature Coefficient resistor. These are pretty neat in that their resistance rises a couple of orders of magnitude at a particular temperature, making overheating easy to detect. However, if the heating is due to overload on the thyristors themselves, it may be too late; some thyristor packs have built in PTCs to improve protection. Of course, the overheating may be due to inadequate cooling for one reason or another; we'll look at this in chapter 10.

Motors are often protected in a similar way, with PTCs embedded in the windings (an option on small motors, standard on large ones). These are connected to a separate protection circuit, or may be connected back to the drive, which will trip or raise a warning as necessary.
PTCs in the motor are notorious sources of interference, and their connections should be screened and kept clear of motor cables (See chapter 10).

For best performance, some drives use linear sensors of various kinds for temperature measurement, as do some motors. Useful if you are doing fancy modelling of the motor and need to know how hot it is.

Over Voltage Protection

We'll see in chapter 7 that there is quite a bit of hardware protection to stop high voltages from damaging the drive, but we also have to consider what happens when the motor regenerates. As mentioned earlier, for an AC drive, the energy comes back to the DC link and charges the DC link capacitor. If the drive has a braking resistor fitted, this will be connected across the link by the chopper IGBT and the voltage will be controlled by simple pulse width modulation as the IGBT turns on and off. If no resistor or chopper is fitted, the drive may try to limit regeneration by speeding up the motor. Makes sense, because if you slow down, you'll get more regeneration. So we have another closed loop controller internal to the drive, which in one way or another is trying to control the DC link voltage during regeneration. If the voltage continues to rise, then the drive will give up and trip, allowing the load to coast (or fall), as mentioned earlier.

Other Protection

There's quite a bit of protection against voltage transients, as well as dust and dirt getting into the electronics, but we'll discuss this in chapter 10. Fusing and protection during fault conditions is another matter; see box: **Not Setting Fire to Your Factory**.

Not Setting Fire to Your Factory

This is a real issue. In the unlikely event (as we always say) of a hardware fault in the power part of a drive, different things can happen. Maybe the fault will clear itself, and present an open circuit. Maybe there'll be a direct short circuit. Or maybe enough current will flow in the fault to start a fire, but not enough to clear a fuse. This is the worst case and it can happen. However, most fires are caused because the installer has not protected the drive properly. Fusing or circuit breakers must be fitted according to the drive manufacturers instructions. There are different types of circuit breakers and fuses, with different protection characteristics, so it's a good idea to follow the recommendations of the supplier, then there's no argument about warranty, and the lawyers won't get involved.

In the early days of thyristors, it was possible to use fuses that would protect the thyristors; these we expensive, and tailored just for this purpose. It isn't possible to protect IGBTs in the same way, partly because they are smaller, more sensitive devices, and partly because the DC link capacitor will provide enough energy to blow them to utter destruction in any case. However, some installers like to fit fast acting fuses simply to reduce damage – which helps with the post mortem on the drive – or to reduce further the possibility of the worst case fault, the current fed fire.

Fuses or circuit breakers are there to protect the wiring and the rest of the cubicle; the drive is already beyond redemption, although at least half the drives that reach the service shop can be economically repaired. In some countries, where import and export is difficult, and labour is cheap, nearly all drives are repaired, but that's another story.

Summary

In the control part of a drive there's quite a lot of peripheral hardware to interface to the outside world. The CPU looks after all this, and nowadays deals with difficult things like timing and protection. An important part of any drive is the closed loop control systems, which will meet the user's needs by maintaining constant speed, torque or whatever else is needed. Closed loop controls can be difficult to stabilise.

Drive and motor protection focuses mainly on preventing them from overheating due to high currents or faulty cooling.

7. AC Drive Control and Construction

Introduction

In chapter 2 we saw how a bridge rectifier, DC link with capacitors, and an inverter consisting of six IGBTs and six commutation diodes made up the basis of the power part of an AC drive. We now need to look more closely at how these components are controlled and packaged, and what additional components and controls are required.
Chapter 6 described in general terms how a drive handles digital and analogue inputs and outputs and other I/O. We also saw how the drive uses open and closed loop control systems, and how it protects itself and the motor.
The block diagram below shows the key functions required in an AC drive controller. The main difference here is that the 'intelligence' is spilt into two parts, for reasons discussed below. Small AC drives tend not to be fitted with encoder interfaces, so this is omitted in comparison with the DC drive control circuitry.

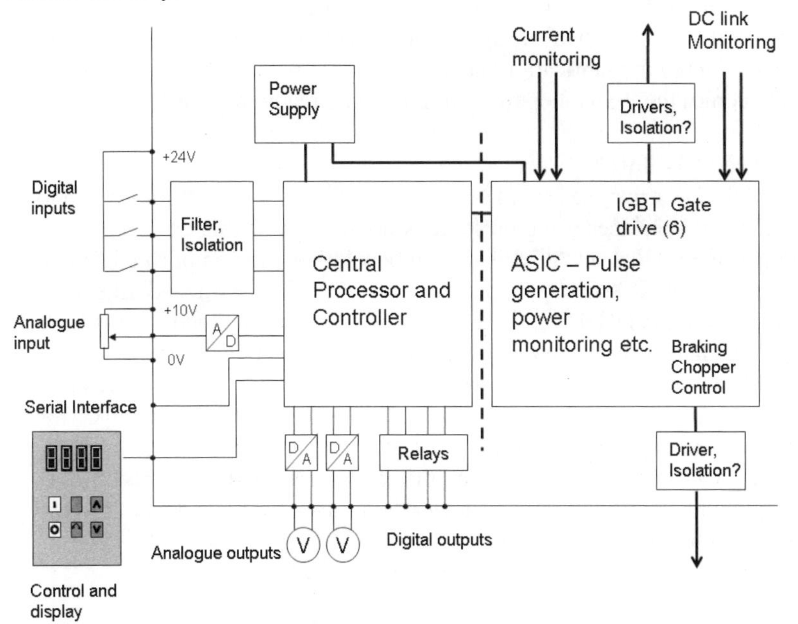

Figure 7.1 AC Drive – Block diagram Control

Intelligent Circuitry – The ASIC

The figure above shows a circuit block labelled ASIC, which stands for Application Specific Integrated Circuit. In other words, a chip that is designed for a specific purpose. The falling costs and ease of design of ASICs have brought about a massive growth in their use in complex electronics from mobile phones to industrial controllers. The development of low cost AC drives would not have been possible without them. We are asking for a component that will at least generate the necessary drive pulses for six (or seven if we count the braking chopper) IGBTs, including deadbands, minimum pulses etc. You can do this with counters, digital comparators (I know - I have) but it is simply not cost effective. Also, as we have the ASIC there, why not get it to do some more work, like measuring the DC link voltage, current monitoring etc? So the ASIC could include as many functions as you can pack onto it. Again, we must trade complexity and development time against cost, reliability – and testability. In practice, in the early days, most manufacturers of drives thought they were pretty smart designing a pulse generator and not much else. These days, every manufacturer has an ASIC with many fancy features built in. The drive designers can work away designing and simulating the chip, sending the design data to the fabrication plant at the last minute. A few weeks later, back comes the ASIC, hopefully bug-free and ready to be tested.

Where to Isolate?

With our DC drive, nearly all our electronics was isolated from the supply, with a few interfaces using pulse transformers or isolating current transformers. With an AC drive it can be a little more complicated. We need to drive the IGBTs with gate pulses of precise pulse width, and, like the thyristors in the DC drive, these IGBTs are connected directly to the high voltage mains supply. Again like the thyristors, some of them are not 'fixed'. In the case of the top devices in each leg, their emitter moves up to the DC link positive when the device is on, and down to the DC link negative when the lower IGBT is turned on. As we drive the gate using a voltage with respect to the emitter, the drive circuit and its supply is jumping all over the place. The lower devices are not so bad, being permanently tied to the DC negative.

We know we must isolate the circuitry that the customer will use (the inputs, outputs, display, communications etc.) but why not put the ASIC, for example, at DC link negative potential, reducing the amount of isolation needed? This idea, and the more conventional arrangement of having all control electronics isolated, is shown below.

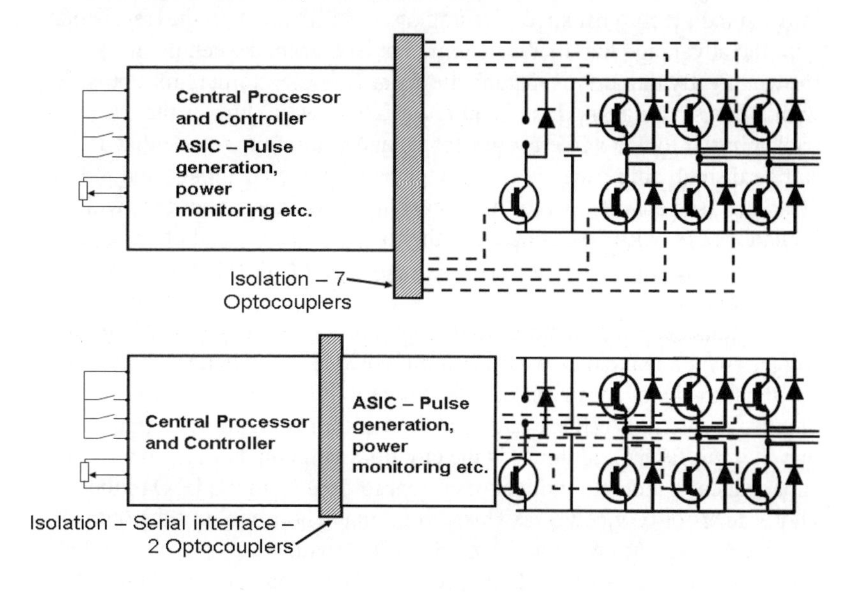

Figure 7.2 AC Drive – Isolation Options

With the first scheme, we have many isolating optocouplers, which must be safety proven, and the creepage and clearance (see chapter 10) across this barrier must meet the relevant safety regulations. If you hold a PCB up to the light you can clearly see the safety isolation gap – usually 5.5 or even 8mm.

In the second scheme, we replace these with just two optocouplers, and we can communicate to our intelligent circuitry on the 'hot' side with a simple serial link, providing we build some more intelligence into the ASIC. However, driving the upper IGBTs is still a little difficult as these are going up and down – but the isolation from DC negative to the drive circuits does not need to meet safety requirements. For more about optocouplers, see box: **Optocouplers**.

Optocouplers

Optocouplers make power electronics a lot easier. The basic principle is pretty straightforward. We have an LED and photosensitive transistor built into a standard chip package. Turning on the LED turns on the transistor, with the advantage that there is significant isolation between them. We've shown already that drives manufacturers are good customers for optos. As with all these things, nothing is quite straightforward. First is the packaging. It took a while for the opto manufacturers to realise that a standard small chip package may not provide enough creepage and clearance (see chapter 10) for drive designers, so they introduced 'wide bodied' packs, with 10mm between the rows of pins instead of 7.5mm. They also obligingly got various safety approvals and tested the isolation to 4 or 5kV.

They also added more features to the opto, putting logic gates or Schmitt triggers which make the switching more positive, but when we started to use them to signal a turn on (or off) to the top IGBT on an inverter, we hit another problem. We'll see later that the top IGBT, its power supply and drive circuit fly up and down as the circuits switch on and off, so any stray capacitance in the opto will cause current to flow from the LED to the phototransistor or vice versa. This current may choose to turn the opto on, off or whatever, not what we want. So, after a while, the opto guys put a screen between the LED and phototransistor or whatever, and achieved amazing Common Mode Rejection (CMR) figures like 25kV/μs. This means if the voltage switches this fast (and this is fast) there won't be any interfering effects.

Another issue with early optos was the differences in on and off times. Optos work in a few hundred nanoseconds, and as long as the on and off times are the same, there's no distortion of the pulse width for the IGBT, but if they are different, the carefully calculated PWM will be distorted. Once these few problems were ironed out, optos became a well-loved friend of the drive designer. The figure below summarises these issues.

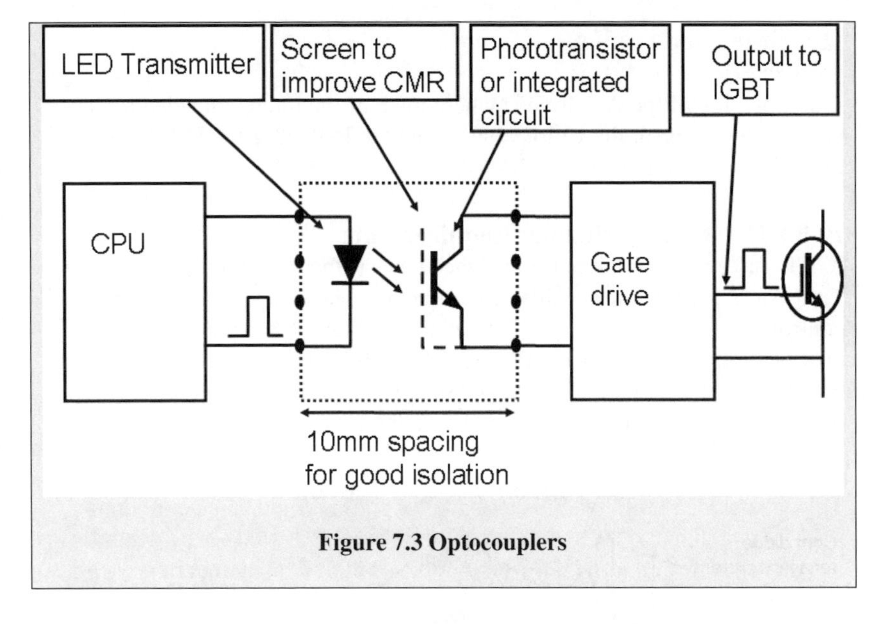

Figure 7.3 Optocouplers

As mentioned before, we must also provide some way of monitoring motor current and DC voltage, so additional signalling and isolation is required. Both schemes are in current use. Where companies are trying to save every penny (or Eurocent or whatever), the cost-balancing act can be quite close. Probably the second arrangement is becoming more common, with cheaper communications available 'on chip'. With this arrangement we are left with a control board with virtually the same electronics as on a DC drive. That is, a display, customer interface, analog and digital inputs and outputs for control and monitoring etc. The ASIC on the 'hot' side now has all sorts of stuff to do. Ironically, the speed and cost of today's microprocessors are so good that it is now close to being cost effective to replace the ASIC with a programmable micro; in the past, a processor simply wasn't fast enough. We'll look at the control side later and the great lump of firmware in the processor itself when we look at practical applications and setting up, but for now let's look at what's on the hot side…

Hot Side Electronics

The 'hot' side of the AC drive is where most of the interesting electronics is: we'll look first at the various bits needed to look after the IGBTs and make the motor turn.

IGBT Drive and Switching Requirements

IGBTs have very high input impedance gates (otherwise they'd be Bipolar Transistors), which are sensitive to static and overvoltage, so we need to control the gate voltage carefully to avoid damage. When we apply a positive voltage (say >3V) to the gate, the IGBT begins to turn on. In practice, a gate drive of 15V or more may be used to ensure good hard turn on. An IGBT switching cycle is shown in the figure below.

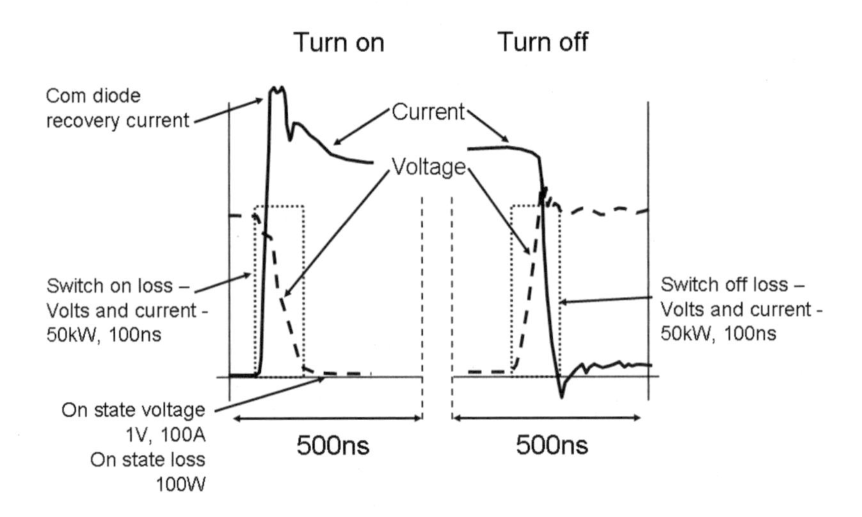

Figure 7.4 IGBT Switching Cycle

When you turn the IGBT on, the voltage across it falls. This takes place pretty quickly, probably within 50 or 100ns, and at the same time the current rises as the IGBT takes over from the com diode conducting the load current. The IGBT also needs to turn the com diode off (see chapter 2), so there is quite a peak of current in the IGBT at turn on, supplying the reverse recovered charge of the diode and, as there is voltage across the device, there is some instantaneous dissipation – that is, a switch on loss.

With the IGBT conducting, however hard we drive it we'll still have an 'on' state voltage across it of maybe a volt or so, so if we are conducting 100A (easily possible in a 37kW drive for example) there is a loss of maybe 100W.
To turn the IGBT off, the gate drive voltage is reduced to zero, and the IGBT turns off. If only. IGBTs are pretty quick, but it takes time to stop the conduction and for the current flow to collapse and divert (to a com diode for example). Although the voltage rises across the collector emitter junction of the IGBT pretty quickly, the current continues to flow, and the current won't think of diverting to a com diode until the IGBT is fully switched off, pushing the voltage at the diode high enough over (or under) the DC link to forward bias the diode. So again we have a period of time when there is a high voltage across the IGBT, but with the load current still in it. Say 500V DC and 100A - this is a 50kW power loss. This dissipation may occur for a hundred nanoseconds at turn off, and again about the same at turn on. So if we switch at 10kHz, then a bit of maths tells us the losses during switching are about 100W (50kW, 200ns, 10,000 times per second). This is pretty neat because power engineers often reckon on the switching losses and 'on' state losses being about equal, as they are here. So there is 200W to get rid of from each IGBT. Actually it's less, because the IGBT only conducts for half the time. This kind of power from a small piece of silicon means mounting and cooling are critical. The drive designer must ensure a good heatsink is provided to get the heat out of the IGBT and into the outside world, maybe with a fan or two. We'll look at this later.

Minimising Losses

We can't do much about the on state loss except pester the IGBT maker to improve his alchemy and reduce the on state voltage. Actually, they do get a little better with time, but it is a slow improvement rather than big breakthroughs. Same with the turn off time and losses. Also, the IGBT tends to slow itself down due to the effect known as 'Miller' Capacitance (named after Mr Capacitance – no Mr Miller actually). At turn off, as the collector voltage rises, the stray capacitance between the collector and the gate means a current flows from the collector to the gate, tending to increase the gate voltage and keep the IGBT turned on. This is countered by having a nice low impedance gate drive to sink any current and hold the voltage low.

There is a similar effect at turn on, so a low impedance drive circuit is required here too. However, fast switching brings its own problems. If we turn on too fast, for example, we'll see a very high current flow into the opposite com diode which may be conducting load current; these problems of diode reverse recovery were described above and in chapter 2. Hopefully we have a diode that has a low reverse charge and a soft, but fast recovery. Even so, it is better to turn the IGBT on a little slowly to control the diode turn off.

As a result of these problems, our gate circuit tends to be a little more complicated than just an on/off voltage on the gate, and we slow the switching by adding resistance to the drive circuits. The IGBT gate essentially looks like a small capacitor, with the added complication of Miller capacitance, so resistors are an easy way to control the switching speed. The figure below shows a typical gate drive circuit. The actual values of the resistors depend on the size of the IGBTs. The ASIC gives a low level as a drive signal, which turns off the buffer transistor, which turns the upper, NPN device on via the 10k resistor. The IGBT gate is then driven directly through the 18R resistor, turning on fairly quickly. At turn off, the buffer pulls base of the PNP driver low, turning it on and pulling the IGBT gate low via the 18R resistor and the 10R resistor in parallel, the diode conducting. So the turn off is lower impedance than the turn on. Selecting these resistor values takes care to get the best switching speed without the problems discussed above. Transistor types are simply the cheapest available.

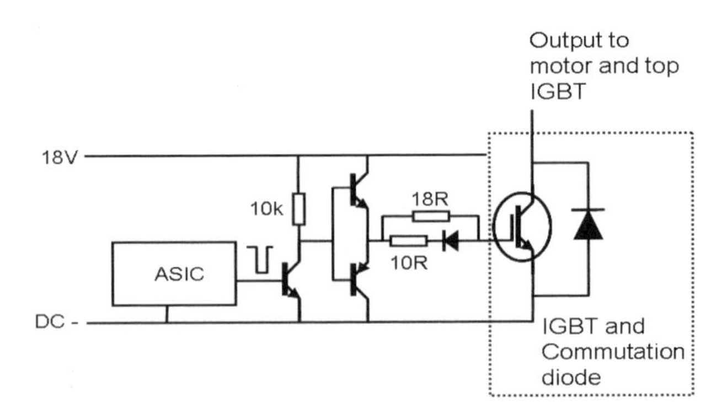

Figure 7.5 Lower Gate Drive Circuit

Power supplies, Bootstrap and Charge pumps

For these gate drive circuits we need a power supply that is connected to the DC link negative for the lower IGBTs, but for the upper IGBTs we need three separate supplies, one for each IGBT. So in total we need four mutually isolated supplies on the 'hot' side. We can achieve this in several ways. A transformer with four separate windings, rectifiers, capacitors and regulators will do a good job, but on low cost drives this is expensive. A cheaper solution is a charge pump, or bootstrap circuit. This is shown in the figure below.

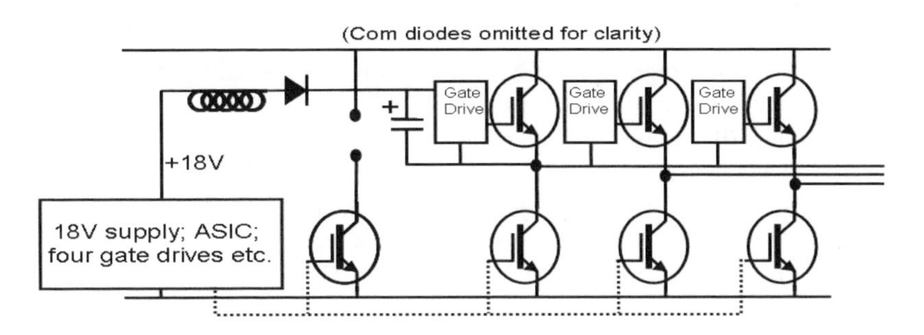

Figure 7.6 Bootstrap Supply for Upper Gate Drives (only one shown)

The trick is to make sure you turn on the bottom IGBTs before you do anything else. This shouldn't cause any problems at switch on. Now the emitter of each upper IGBT is connected to DC negative. The bootstrap diode conducts, and tops up the capacitor to the required voltage – say 18V. The little surface mount inductor just limits the current spike on the main (DC negative) 18V supply. Turn off the lower IGBT, and the upper IGBT, with its charged gate drive supply capacitor, floats up and the diode reverse biases. Now the gate circuit has enough charge on its capacitor to drive the IGBT a couple of times, until we turn the lower IGBT on again. Fortunately our PWM schemes have lots of switching events to keep the capacitor pumped up, although we may need to be careful using FLB modulation (see chapter 5). Each upper IGBT needs its own bootstrap circuit as each emitter is connected to a different phase of the motor.

Of course, the 18V supply must come from somewhere; let's look at the power supplies and the requirements.

Power Supplies

We clearly need an isolated, low voltage power supply for the customer interface electronics on the 'safe' side of the drive. We also need at least one supply on the 'hot' side to drive the IGBTs. We'll see later that we may need even more supplies on the hot and safe side. So it looks like we'll need several isolated, regulated low voltage supplies.
Like early DC drives, some early AC drives used conventional 50Hz transformers with several secondary windings with rectifiers, capacitors, voltage regulators etc. These are quick and easy to design, but have several disadvantages.

- The linear regulators dissipate a lot of heat, especially if we have to design for wide supply variations – say 380 – 500V.
- The 50Hz transformers are big, although at least this makes safety clearances easy.
- If the supply fails, the different low voltage supplies will collapse at different rates, even if the DC link stays high due to a light load. This can cause unpredictable results (IGBT failures).

A more modern solution presents itself; the switched mode power supply (SMPS). An SMPS is now pretty straightforward to design, especially now that IGBTs or MOSFETs are available to operate with DC link voltages up to 1000V. With improved magnetics and better control chips, the clever bit is designing a transformer with several outputs which is small, low cost and meets the necessary safety clearances. An SMPS that runs off the DC link has the advantage that if the supply fails, the SMPS will keep running from the DC link capacitor until the DC reaches quite a low level. This discharges the DC link, or allows the drive to keep running through short mains breaks. You can even set the drive up so that it powers itself during breaks by regenerating from the motor, charging the DC link capacitor from the kinetic energy in the load. (see chapter 8). A block diagram of a typical power supply is shown below.

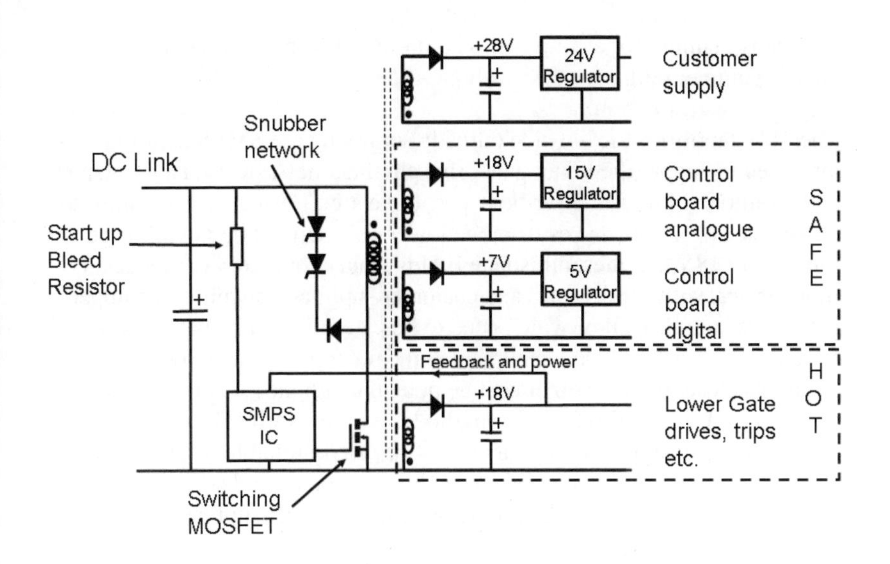

Figure 7.7 Power Supply Block diagram

In this case, a high voltage MOSFET transistor is used to switch a standard flyback transformer (see chapter 2), which effectively serves as a smoothing inductor for the secondary supplies. The MOSFET may need a little heatsink to keep it cool. The MOSFET is controlled by a standard SMPS control chip, which starts up with a bleed from the DC link, but is then powered by the 18V secondary supply. This supply is also the feedback for the power supply system; the chip controls the pulse width of the IGBT to keep this 18V constant. Consequently, the chip regulates all the secondary supplies pretty well, although cross regulation can be a problem if the loads on the other supplies vary too much.

There are at least three other secondary windings, two of which supply the control board with regulated 5 and 15V for the control board electronics. A separate, isolated 24V supply may also be provided for use by the customer. Some drives have isolated inputs on the control board, so this supply is also used to power the customer side of these. The 24V may also power communication modules, encoders etc. The linear regulator is important here as the customer may short circuit or overload the supply.

Any additional supplies may be derived from existing supplies; for example, a precision 10V supply is made available to the customer to connect to a potentiometer if a 0 – 10V signal is required to control the motor speed.

A negative supply for a couple of op amps can also be generated with a charge pump circuit.

The 18V supply on the hot side (already supplying the SMPS controller) is also used to supply the lower gate drive circuits, the ASIC (via a regulator) and monitoring circuits described later. If we aren't using charge pumps to power the upper gate drives from the lower 18V supply, then we'll need three more 18V supplies, all isolated. This makes for a very complicated transformer, with 'hot', 'safe' and customer supplies, as well as the upper gate drive supplies, all of which need to be carefully isolated and checked for cross interference. You can imagine the potential noise problems as windings close to one another change potential at hundreds of volts per microsecond as the IGBTs and com diodes do their stuff. The power supply needs careful design, and of course must be utterly reliable. Fortunately, there are good control chips and MOSFETs available, and some transformer manufacturers understand the problems of drive power supplies.

Voltage Monitoring

We need to monitor the DC link voltage in order to trip the drive if the voltage gets too high due to regeneration. If it gets too high because the supply has risen out of limits, we can't do much about it, but tripping the drive anyway seems like a good idea to reduce the chance of damage.
If we have an ASIC with some intelligence – especially maybe an A to D which is at DC negative potential, then voltage monitoring is pretty straightforward with some high value resistors from the DC positive. The ASIC continually monitors the DC link voltage and periodically passes the information back to the CPU over the serial link. If the ASIC detects a high voltage, it can turn off the IGBTs directly, and then inform the control circuits via the internal interface. The main microprocessor can then raise an alarm via the display or other external communications.
If we don't have an A to D available on the 'hot' side, we can use a differential amplifier on the 'safe' side, fed with high value 'safe' resistors. The resistors should meet the creepage and clearance requirements to maintain the safety barrier; I'd put a few in series myself; in any case this is a requirement in the safety standards.
This arrangement is shown in the figure below.

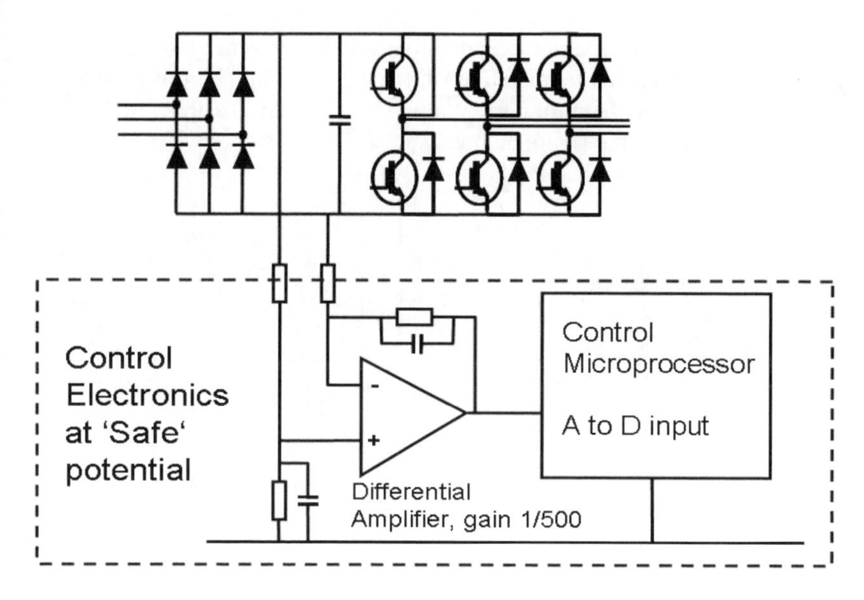

Figure7.8 Voltage Monitoring

Looks OK, but there's a snag. The resistors present a high, but measurable impedance between the DC link – the mains – and the 'safe' control circuit. In some applications, notably on ships, this leakage is not acceptable, at least not when you have lots of drives creating parallel paths, and therefore a lower resistance. Modern cruise ships have a lot of ventilation equipment, controlled by drives. See the problem? Clearly if your measurement is all on the 'hot' side there isn't a problem. Just another consideration, which is hopefully taken into account at the design stage.

Current Monitoring

We need to monitor the current to have some idea of the torque, as well as to protect the motor and the inverter. Ideally, we'll measure or calculate the motor currents in each phase, and use this information to derive the torque, the loading on the motor, and maybe even the motor temperature if we've built up a history of the current. We'll also have to have some form of very fast protection that trips the inverter in a matter of microseconds in the event of a short circuit in the motor cable or windings. We have to think about short circuits to ground as well as between the motor phases.

We may also get clever and calculate if our IGBTs are getting too hot; monitoring the heatsink temperature isn't fast enough for short overloads. So what options are there for current monitoring? Lots! Possible monitor points are shown in the figure below.

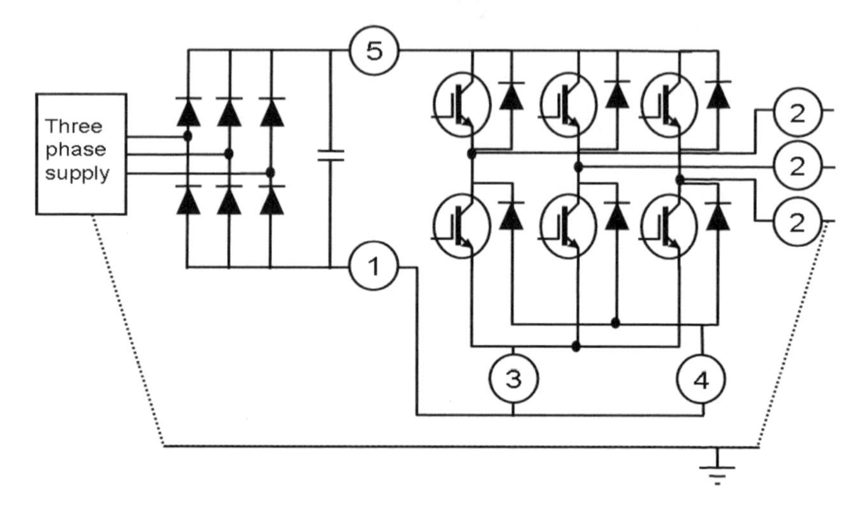

Figure 7.9 Current monitoring

Five monitoring points are shown:

1. DC Link Negative Monitoring
   This is good, because we have a supply and some electronics, so we can feed the signal into an A to D (or buffer amplifier or something) and pass it back up to the control electronics via a serial connection. If we don't have an ASIC, we could, for example, run a V to f converter or pulse width modulator and pass the information through an optocoupler back to the control electronics. However, while it is clear that all the current flowing here eventually ends up in the motor (where else would it go?), deriving the motor current from the signal here is difficult. The current is complex, as it flows back and forth from the capacitor through the com diodes. Also, at low speeds the current pulses can be narrow, making measurement difficult.

2. Motor Current Measurement.
   Another good place to measure. Here we can measure the motor currents directly, and we only need to measure two phases, because the three must add up to zero. But we need two measurement systems instead of one, and the outputs are floating up and down, needing isolation.

3 and 4. Emitter and Com diode measurement.
   This has advantages like (1), but measurement is much easier as the positive (IGBT) and negative (com diode) currents are separated. Two measuring systems are needed again, at DC negative potential.

5. DC Link Positive Monitoring.
   This has the same measurement properties as (1), but is at DC positive potential, which makes measurement even harder.

The reason for including (5) here is that we need to protect the drive against short circuits, including short circuits to ground. If we short circuit two of the outputs, the current will come from the DC link positive and flow back to DC negative. However, if we short circuit to ground, the dotted line shows the circuit will go back to the supply transformer, where the neutral point is (hopefully) grounded, through the rectifiers, and down one DC link arm, depending on which rectifier, positive or negative, is conducting at the time. Trace it though. So we need to cover the case of flow through the positive of the DC link by the addition of a current monitor there. Of course, for short circuit monitoring, we only need a go/no go circuit, but it does need to be fast.

We now need to think about our measurement and isolation systems. What options are there for accurate measurement (for indication and torque calculations) and go/no go (for tripping quickly following a short circuit? Many drives use Hall effect sensors for current measurement. Hall effect sensors detect a small voltage produced in a conductor at right angles to current flow when the conductor is in a magnetic field. Named after Edwin Hall, an American physicist, bless him. These sensors have the advantage that they look like a current transformer (the larger ones anyway) so the cable is pushed through the hole and a voltage generated proportional to current. They have a good frequency response, and provide an isolated signal, but can be expensive for small drives.

A current to voltage converter, or resistor as we call it, is a lower cost solution. A low value resistor, a bit of filtering and a comparator driving an optocoupler are enough to serve as a go/no go signal for short circuit protection in the output, or more usually, in the DC link. Where no power supply is available (i.e in the upper DC link trip) you can maybe get away with a transistor junction as a reference coupled directly to an optocoupler. Talking of optos, a neat variation on the optocoupler provides accurate current measurement instead of a Hall effect sensor. If we connect a low value resistor in series with the motor output connection, then using our bootstrap or floating supply provided for the upper IGBT, we can power a simple A to D (e.g. sigma delta – see chapter 6) converter, and drive an optocoupler with the resultant pulses. The isolated output of the opto (a pulse stream) can then be fed directly into the control processor and interpreted by software to give a current value. If this sounds like a lot of components, the opto manufacturer has integrated them into a single component with suitable creepage and clearance, and priced it to be competitive with Hall effect sensors.

OK, so what's the bottom line with current monitoring?

The emitter and com diode current sensing is pretty neat, and there are plenty of patents to infringe here, but, as IGBTs and com diodes are usually packaged up and connected together, if you want to separate these connections you'll need to discuss it with the manufacturer of the power semiconductors. This will certainly add to the cost, as for a range of drives you'll need a range of special packages.

For smaller drives, we can use low value resistors (they look a bit like metal links on pcbs) and the fancy optos with built in converters in two of the three output leads. They're a bit slow on their own for short circuits, so we'll need some simple go/no go trip circuits in the top and bottom of the DC link to protect against short circuits. Incidentally, position these properly and they'll protect the braking chopper (omitted in these figures) against short circuits as well. For larger drives we can use a lot of resistors in parallel, or go back to Hall effect devices.
Measuring current and getting isolation, and providing an accurate and rapidly responding signal is never easy, and the high speed, high power switching of the IGBTs with their narrow pulses causes many problems, overcome by experience and hard graft.

Power Stack Data

One of the smaller items on the power part of the electronics will be a small memory containing the power stack data. On power up, the control board will read this to find out what sort of power electronics is on the board, and it will then select the appropriate settings for operation. This means the control board can be swapped from one drive to another without reprogramming. Also, during manufacture, it isn't necessary to pair the power part and the control board; the power stack memory will take care of that. The memory contains such things as maximum output current, operating voltage, maximum temperature etc. But it will also set the maximum switching frequency (which may be 16kHz for a 750W drive and 4kHz for a 75kW drive), the deadband time, and may also contain information about the overload capability of the IGBTs to improve their protection. If there is an ASIC, the ASIC may help to communicate this information to the control board. If not, then the power stack data may be physically on the power part of the drive, but electrically connected to the control board. Of course, this needs extra connections between the two, and attention to creepage and clearance to this 'safe' circuitry on the power board.

Rectifier and DC Link Components

We've looked at the detail of the inverter part of the drive, but we shouldn't forget the rather boring rectifier and DC link capacitors, as well as any protection and filtering components. Together these can take up quite a bit of room in a drive and may also dissipate heat.

Diode Rectifier

This is pretty boring actually. As explained in chapter 2, we need six diodes if we have a three phase supply, only four if single phase. Like IGBTs, all diodes are supplied in isolated packages, with 6, 4 or 2 to a pack, depending on power rating. This makes mounting on the same heatsink as the IGBTs pretty straightforward.
The voltage rating of the diodes will probably be 1400V for a three phase 400V drive. This allows for the voltage transients that often occur on industrial supplies, but additional protection is always added (see later). Diodes are pretty rugged and pretty reliable.

DC link Capacitor

As mentioned in chapter 5, the DC link capacitor does several jobs.

- It acts as a low impedance source for the high frequency currents that flow back and forth from the inverter.
- It provides some hold up for short supply dropouts, allowing the drive to keep running for a short time. For a drive fed by a single phase supply, a large capacitor is needed to hold up between half cycle peaks.
- It will absorb some regenerative energy from the motor, at least until the braking chopper starts operating.
- It offers some protection to the inverter, as it will absorb some surges and transients from the supply, although the rectifier diodes have to carry this as far as the capacitor without damage.

Most DC link capacitors are PCB mounting nowadays, with more pins than needed electrically in order to provide mounting strength. High voltage capacitors are available, but 400V units seem to be preferred. For three phase 400V drives (DC link 560V and more) pairs are connected in series with voltage balancing resistors in parallel, which also discharge the capacitors on power down after the SMPS has shut off.

Losses and Efficiency

We've mentioned several times that the drive is full of losses; the switching and 'on' state losses of the IGBTs and diodes, the capacitor losses, not forgetting the steady state losses of the electronics and power supply, the fan, the display etc. We'll see in chapter 9 that drives are often sold as energy savers, so it's clear that minimising losses is important. High losses aren't very good when you're putting a drive in a cubicle or machine; the temperature can soon build up (see chapter 10)
So drive designers try to reduce losses by optimising the power supply (then the specification says you must be able to power such and such an encoder and an interface module, making the power supply bigger again) or getting the best IGBTs – at a price. As a result, the marketing guys say how efficient the drive is – say 96%. On this basis, a 7.5kW drive loses 4% or 300W right? Wrong. 7.5kW is the mechanical power output of the motor.

The motor may be 90% efficient, so there is 8.3kW going into it. The motor is also drawing a magnetising current, and therefore has a power factor of (say) 0.8. Maybe we should look at the full load current of the motor and relevant voltage. 19A at 400V, throw in a √3, and we get about 13kVA. 4% of this is 520W. This makes a bit more sense, as the total current, rather than the real power, will set the losses. If you are concerned about losses, it's probably best to get the manufacturer to tell you the losses in watts, rather than try to work back from the 'marketing' efficiency. Remember these losses are calculated probably at continuous full load, nominal input voltage (although voltage doesn't affect the losses too much); your operating condition may well be different. Losses will rise rapidly during overload, but the drive takes care of itself (and the motor) here.

Protection and Filtering

Electromagnetic compatibility (EMC) is an important consideration for designers and users of drives, and we'll discuss it in detail in chapter 10. Many drives have built in filters to ensure they comply with the levels laid down by law in many countries. These filters are deceptively simple C - L – C (π) filters. Designing these is a real skill, as regulations require measurement of interference levels up to 1GHz, which sneaks around the best inductor, and sees a few millimetres of PCB track as impedance. More of this later! The figure below shows a typical filter, along with the protection components, DC link capacitors and rectifier discussed in this section.

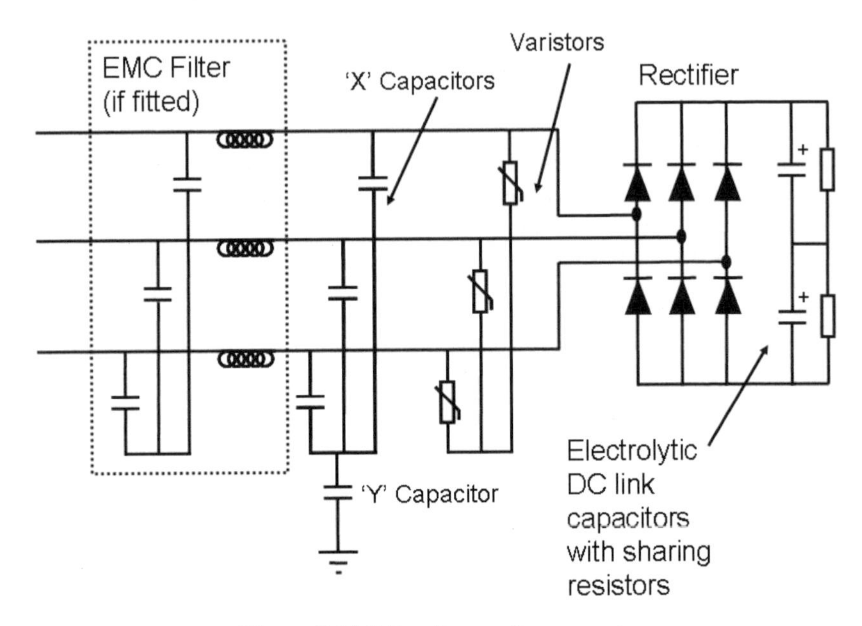

Figure 7.10 Other Power Components

The filter capacitors must be selected for their high frequency characteristics (some capacitors look inductive at high frequencies) and must be designed for connection across the supply (so called 'X' capacitors). The inductor is a balanced core inductance. This means, because all the low frequency currents are equal and opposite, the core can be very small as the average flux is very low. For unbalanced currents – that is currents that flow in the protective earth connection, the impedance is much higher. A lot of interference currents flow in the ground line, so this is a good arrangement. Of course, the impedance is also high at higher frequencies, which we want to block. These cores are generally toroidal, and may be potted to make mounting easier and reduce noise. A filter is usually a built in option for a drive. External filters can be added to reduce further the conducted interference in order to meet stiffer regulations, see chapter 10.

Additional Protection

Experience suggests that, even if a filter is not fitted, it's a good idea to try to mop up some of the high frequency interference going in and out of the drive. We'll look at this in chapter 10. So line to line, or line to star point 'X' capacitors are often fitted, as well as capacitors between the supply and ground, cunningly known as 'Y' capacitors. 'Y' capacitors are designed to meet more regulations concerning components connected from live to ground, in particular, they shouldn't fail short circuit. In this circuit, a single 'Y' capacitor is connected from the star point of the 'X' capacitors. Cheaper than three, and less stressed. The 'X' capacitors form part of the EMC filter if it is fitted.

Finally, to absorb any high voltage spikes from lightning or inductive switching elsewhere in the plant, the incoming connections are fitted with varistors. Varistors are non linear resistors, a bit like back to back Zener diodes; they'll start to conduct at a particular voltage. They are very fast, but unlike Zeners, are soft, so a varistor rated at 550V AC will start conducting seriously at about 1000V, hopefully below the failure voltage of the rectifiers. Varistors will also wear out, that is, if there are too many transients they will give up and turn the colour of burnt toast, with the rectifiers and drive going the same way shortly afterwards.

Supply Voltages: 230, 400 or what?

Drives are mainly designed for industrial applications, and most, but by no means all such installations have a three phase supply around about 400V (See chapter 1). At high powers, say above 37kW, the currents and therefore losses are so high it's not really practical to build a lower voltage (i.e. 230V) drive. Perhaps it's surprising they even go that high. The reason is that there are a few countries that distribute 230V three phase, so there is a bit of a market there. More important are lower power applications – say below 3kW – or where single phase 230V is only available such as small workshops, farms, commercial, or even domestic applications. These 230V drives tend to be single or three phase input, although if a filter is included two versions may be offered to keep the cost down as a three phase input filter is a bit pricey. For some reason, 230V drives are significantly cheaper than 400V units of the same power; it may be forced by the market, as the component cost doesn't vary that much (after all, current is higher). Below 1kW, 230V and 400V drives are sold in about equal numbers. Designs may need to vary significantly between these drives, as, for example, some cost effective power supply controllers may not be available at 400V AC (560V DC link).

All this keeps designers busy, and when they've finished the 230V and 400V versions, some sales guy will explain how he could sell thousands of drives if only he had a 690V version/a 575V version for Canada/a 230V 55kW version/a 400V single phase version.... etc. Sometimes someone believes him, invests time and money in development and well, you can guess; he sells 15 drives in three years. Some sales guys will argue that you need to offer a full range of products like this to be credible in the market; actually a more convincing argument.
Even without this influence, by the time you have 230 and 400V, maybe single and three phase, filtered and unfiltered, maybe IP20 and IP56 (see chapter 3), you have hundreds of different part numbers and something to keep production and planning engineers busy.

Putting it all Together

This lot needs to be assembled (quickly and easily) into something which is compact, easy to install, has a good flow of cooling air, convenient terminals for connection, a display and human interface (buttons!) that is easy to read and use, and (dare I say it) looks neat. For a large drive with a big heatsink, there is plenty of room, but for a small drive this can be quite a challenge. The fashion for smaller and smaller (credit card footprint!) drives seems to have passed, and achievable sizes are in vogue, but size, or more importantly panel footprint is still important. Electrical cabinets tend to be pretty deep, in electronic terms at least, so book shaped units (mounted as on a bookshelf) make good use of space, but if displays and useable terminals are to be included, let alone cooling fans, these designs can prove difficult. So, let's summarise what we have to include:

- Control board, probably with customer signal terminals
- Display and button board
- Power board, with major 'hot ' side components, probably mains supply and motor terminals. Filters and DC link capacitors may need to be separate on larger units
- Heatsink – generally the IGBTs will be sandwiched between the heatsink and power board.
- Fan – maybe two
- Interconnections – cables, flexible PCB, or motherboard.
- Cover to keep fingers out.
- The dreaded creepage and clearances must be maintained for safety and reliability (see chapter 10).

There are many other detail considerations such as stopping dust building up on high voltage parts, EMC limitations, where to put the rating label, and making the fan easy to replace. And, worst of all, it has to meet the corporate image in terms of colour and design. However, the figure below shows several ways of putting a small drive together to meet the needs of the customer at a reasonable cost. The result is a compact unit designed for installation in an electrical cabinet or customer's machine. Units designed for mounting outside of cabinets are usually larger, and have a higher degree of protection; these designs are IP20 protection (see chapter 3).

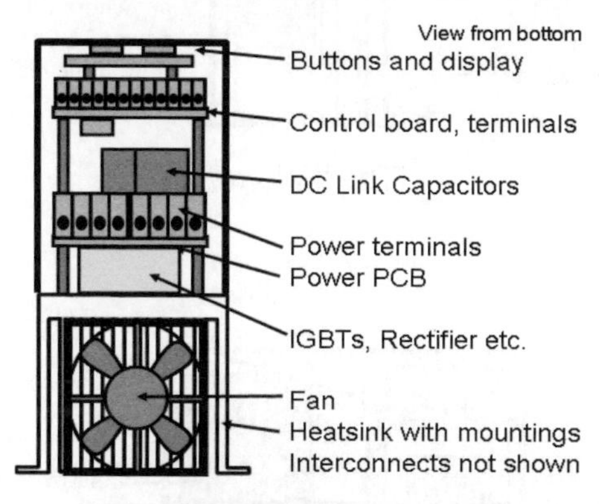

The 'Multi Storey'

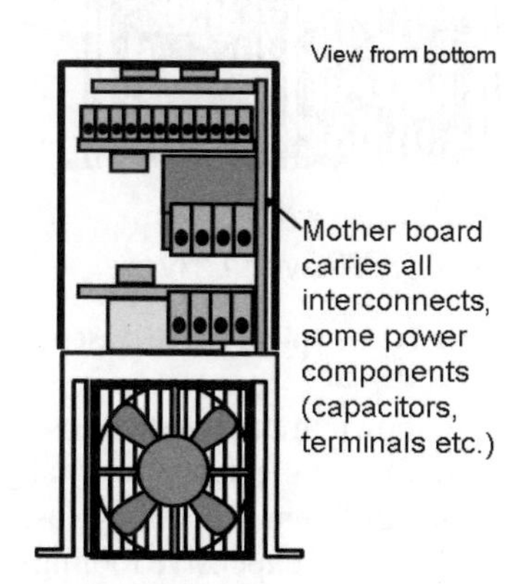

The 'Mother board'

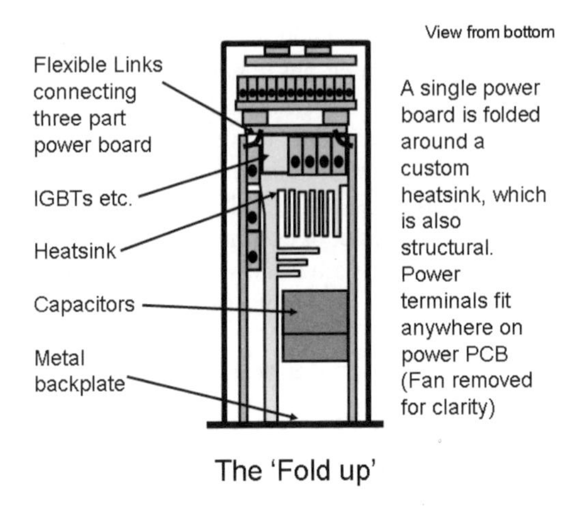

The 'Fold up'

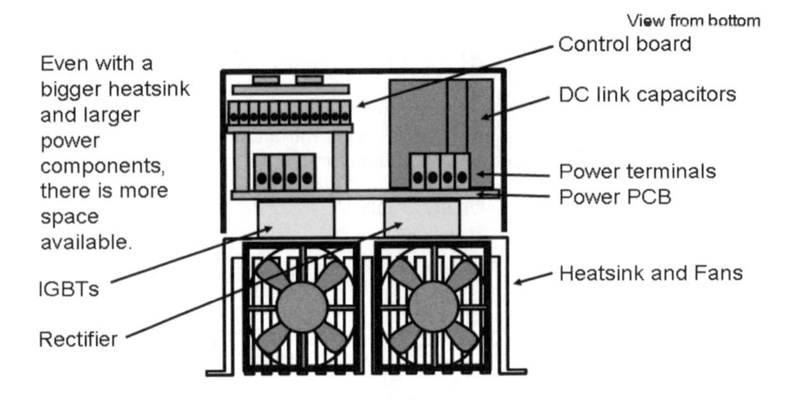

The High Power Drive

Figure 7.11 Typical Drive Assemblies

A typical product range is shown in the figure below. These products use as many common parts as possible to create a power range between 120W and 200kW. Nevertheless, many different heatsinks, plastic mouldings and pressed metal parts (which require expensive tooling) are required to complete the range.

Setting the break points in the design, where you go up a 'frame' size is critical, as you wish to minimise the number of sizes (there are eight in this range), but if the competitor's 22kW is smaller than yours this is a disadvantage. If we wish to offer product variations, such as different voltage ranges, different filter options, or pump and fan variants (see chapter 8) clearly the whole business becomes more complicated.

Figure 7.12 Typical Product Range

Summary

To design and manufacture a practical cost effective drive, the designer must decide how to split his circuit between the 'hot' side and 'safe' parts. He or she will have to design a decent power supply that somehow powers the upper IGBT drive circuits. Monitoring and protection circuits will be needed, and the whole thing, including the DC capacitors cooling parts and controls must be sensibly packaged.

8. Features, Functions and Jargon

Introduction

In many ways our AC Drive is a power amplifier. It takes a speed demand (often 0 – 10V) and converts it into a power signal of variable voltage and frequency that will control the speed of the motor connected to it. But of course more than simple amplification is demanded. Acceleration and deceleration rates would be nice. The ability to trim the output voltage is useful to get the best torque performance. Protection levels for motor current must be set. Once we start looking at applications, we start with "Wouldn't it be nice". Wouldn't it be nice if we could work with a series of fixed speeds for our lathe? Wouldn't it be nice if we could set a minimum frequency on our fan? Wouldn't it be nice if we had different settings when we use a different motor? Etc. Of course, it's only software. A few keystrokes and there is another feature that may sell a few more drives. Over the years, these extra bits build into a monster that means a manual listing all the settings will run to several hundred or more pages for a simple drive. Great; the drive can probably meet the customer's application, but he may not be able to find the feature, let alone set it up.
This chapter attempts to explain some of these features, how they are implemented in drives, and where they might be used. We'll start with the simple features and work up, trying to explain any jargon along the way. As different companies use different words for the same function, we'll try to pick these up as well.

Selecting and Setting - Parameters and Programming

Everybody wants a drive that is easy to set up and optimise for his or her application. Although there have been attempts to automate commissioning, in general users must still set the acceleration rates, current limits etc.for themselves. Each setting is usually available in a parameter and can be changed as described in chapter 6. The methods vary for different drives; there are many variants like read only parameters that give information; there are sub sets of parameters that can be selected in different ways, but the principles are similar. Setting up can, of course be carried out using a PC, a PLC programming tool, and with some drives, a handheld device.

As mentioned earlier, many drives offer enhanced control panels with text and help screens, but for many simple applications the standard buttons and simple display are enough to commission the drive.

Basic Features and Functions

Motor settings

For even the simplest application, we need to make some basic adjustments to ensure good performance and protection for the motor, load and drive. We need to tell the drive a bit about the motor.
It's usually a good idea to programme the drive with the motor rating plate data, or at least some of it. If you load the motor voltage and nominal frequency, the drive will select a suitable V to f relationship to maintain the optimum flux at all speeds (but see later). If the power factor (Cos φ) is loaded, the drive will have more information about the magnetising current in the motor. The power rating will give some information about the size of the motor.

However, after the voltage and frequency, probably the most important information is the full load current of the motor. We discussed in previous chapters about protecting the motor and drive, but the protection will be useless if the correct motor data, particularly the motor full load current, is not programming into the drive. The protection software will then allow overload as described in chapter 6, getting the maximum out of the motor without burning it out. Hopefully! You'll find these functions described as Current Limit, Motor Protection, i^2t protection, Thermal overload protection and so on.

Normally, of course, a 7.5kW drive will be preset with the data for a 'standard' 7.5kW motor, but it's always worth checking as motor data varies quite a lot, particularly for newer, high efficiency motors.
If you use a 5.5kW motor with a 7.5kW drive, then changing the settings is essential, otherwise the drive will happily allow the 5.5kW motor to burn out, thinking it has the capabilities of a 7.5kW motor.

Remember if you are working with a 60Hz motor you'll need to set the 60Hz values from the rating plate. Many drives have a parameter that selects between 50 and 60Hz operation, and changes lots of settings, such as kilowatts to horsepower, maximum frequency etc. at the same time. This may or may not suit you, but remember it is the motor frequency that matters; the applied mains frequency is rectified and doesn't matter here. So if you build machines with 50Hz motors and export them to 60Hz countries you use the 50Hz settings.

Controlling the drive

How do we want to control the drive? We have digital inputs, analogue inputs, and serial communications maybe. A simple solution, and maybe the default setting, is to control the drive from the front panel terminals, which may offer start, stop, 'speed up' and 'slow down' buttons. This is great if you've just connected the drive up, and you want to see if it works, but if you want your machine or control system to run the drive, you'll need to change some settings. The default settings of digital inputs will probably allow the connection of a simple run/stop switch to one of them; high to run, low to stop, usually using one of the local 24V supplies available on a terminal. Alternatively, an external voltage can be applied to the input, or the output from a PLC connected. We can use more digital inputs to reverse the drive, clear faults, select fixed frequencies or change more complex functions; it is just a matter of setting up.

If you want to use a momentary action push button you may need to do a bit more programming, as you'll want the drive to react to edges, rather than levels. You can use momentary action buttons to increase and decrease frequency as well; this is referred to in some drives as the 'motor pot' function as it mimics the old controllers that used a motorised potentiometer to increase or decrease speed, like the remote volume control on my hifi. 'Turn off' commands tend to be defaulted to active low; that is, you need a high state on the input to keep the drive running. That way if the wire breaks the drive stops.

Many drives offer a 'jog' or 'inch' feature as a button on the control panel or as a digital input programming option. This will run the drive at a preset speed – usually a low one – to jog or inch the machine into position. It's also useful to check everything is working.

Controlling the setpoint

We can adjust the setpoint using the up and down buttons described above, but it is more often adjusted using an analogue input. Remember the setpoint is the value that is wanted; in a simple system this will be the output frequency of the drive; in a more complex system it may be a conveyer speed or a temperature. Looking simply at the drive and motor here, it is the output frequency of the drive.

We can vary the analogue input, and therefore the setpoint, using a locally mounted potentiometer and voltage reference from a terminal, or we can connect a remote signal from a PLC. The default setting for the input will usually be 0 – 10V, which produces 0 – 50Hz. Current inputs of 0 – 20mA, or 4 – 20mA may also be available as discussed earlier.

On most drives the analogue input can be scaled to suit the application, and a second analogue input may be provided to accommodate a signal from a sensor – this is useful for closed loop control systems, described in chapter 6. Some of the possible set ups for simple control of a drive are shown in the figures below.

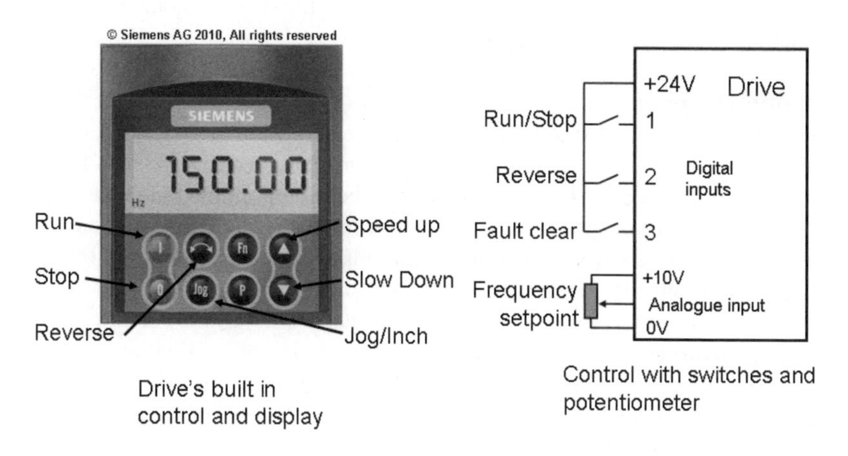

Figure 8.1 Simple Control – Control Panel and Switches

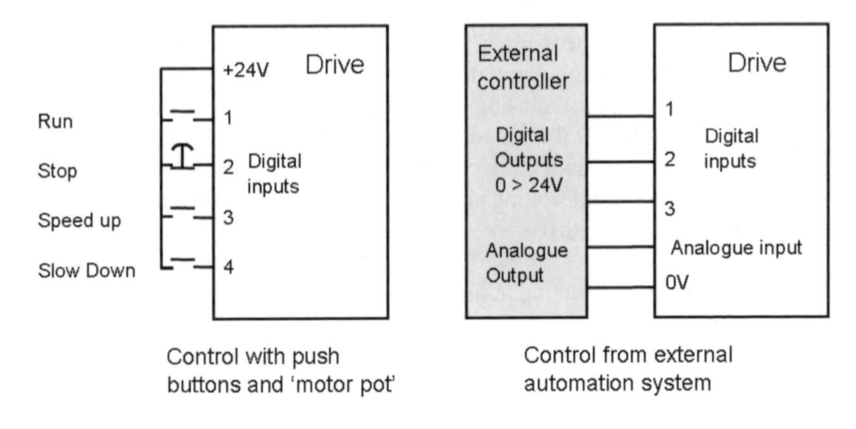

Figure 8.2 Simple Control – Push buttons and External Controller

Fixed frequencies are sometimes preferable to continuously variable control, and in this case the setpoint is selected using suitably programmed digital inputs. Variations on this theme include binary coding of digital inputs and whether the run/stop signal is separate or part of the fixed frequency function.

Digital Outputs

In chapter 6 we mentioned that the drive has one or more digital outputs, often relays. By default, the outputs may be programmed to indicate a fault or alarm, if one occurs, but they can usually be reprogrammed to show overload, maximum speed reached, drive running etc. They can often also be configured to control a electrometrical brake (see later). Surprisingly useful once you start to use them.

Accelerating the Motor and Load

We saw in chapter 1 that mass has inertia, and that inertia in a rotating mass depends on the shape of the mass, leading to the property 'moment of inertia'. Therefore when we accelerate a load we will need torque to accelerate both the inertia of the mass, and the moment of inertia of any rotating masses. In a conveyer system for example, there will be the mass of the belt, and anything on it, as well as the moment of inertia of the rollers, the gearbox parts, and the motor itself. A fan has a very high moment of inertia, and may require a long acceleration (and deceleration) time for this reason.

We'll need torque for the load itself as well – lifting the material, moving the air etc. The sum of the accelerating and load torque should be taken account when selecting a drive for a particular application.

In any case, starting a drive at an output frequency of, say, 50Hz on a stopped motor would draw a high current, maybe tripping the drive, as well as shocking the load unnecessarily. As mentioned earlier, a smooth, low current start is sometimes enough reason to fit a drive in place of direct on line or star/delta starting.

All drives allow an acceleration rate to be programmed. This is usually set as the time to reach the maximum frequency, and is also called the ramp up time. A typical default value may be 10 seconds (to 50Hz) for a small drive, or up to 60 seconds for a large drive, where higher inertias can be expected.

However, a small packing machine may use a motor to fold a cover as quickly as possible; here a ramp up time of 0.2 seconds may be set if the load and inertia are small. On the other hand, a centrifuge may need a ramp up of several minutes; in this case, the inertia and required acceleration rate sets the motor size. Of course, slower ramp up times may also be selected for smooth, jerk free operation for other reasons. Talking of jerk, most drives include a smoothing, or rounding feature. Now jerk is the rate of change of acceleration, so for a smooth start in a lift, or on a conveyer (so the bottles don't fall over) smoothing brings on, and takes off, the acceleration gently.

Most drives have the ability to select different acceleration (and deceleration) rates for different applications. You may need to run a machine up and down at a different rate during a cleaning cycle; you can choose different ramp rates at this time using a digital input or serial control for example. Can be handy.

The figure below shows how ramp rates are defined, and how smoothing affects them.

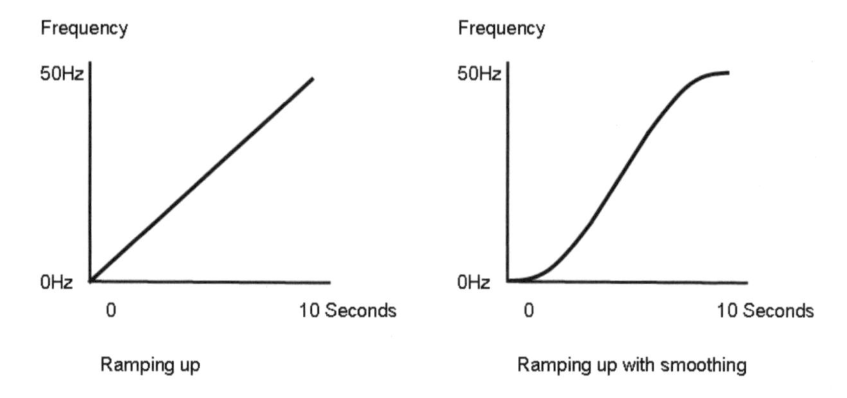

Figure 8.3 Acceleration and Smoothing

In summary, if you need fast acceleration, you'll need to look at the total inertia of the system, as well as the steady load, and select a motor with enough torque. If acceleration is not important, keep it nice and slow.

Deceleration and Stopping

Deceleration is set up in the same kind of way as acceleration and it is logically referred to as ramp down. However, we still have inertias to deal with, but in this case the inertia of the load will cause the motor to regenerate, returning energy to the drive. We've seen that, if this happens, the voltage on the DC link capacitor rises, and if no braking chopper and braking resistance are fitted, the drive may trip. This will happen if we slow the motor down by reducing the setpoint, or if we give normal stop command, which ramps the setpoint down to 0Hz and then turns off the drive.

So we need to think about our options for decelerating and stopping:

1. If the load is pretty low inertia, or if there is a lot of losses or load (like in a mixer or conveyer system for example) then we can ramp down pretty quickly following a stop command or setpoint change without too many problems. With a high inertia load we may be still be OK with a long ramp down time if that's acceptable.
2. If we aren't bothered about stopping times, or if we are using an external brake of some sort, we can disable the drive with our off command instead of starting a ramp down. With no output on the drive, the flux in the motor will collapse, and the motor and load are just deadweight. Now the motor and load will coast to a stop in its own time, or we can apply our brake. This is sometimes called an off 2 or freewheel stop. This is a little uncontrolled, as you don't really know how long it will take to stop.
3. We can use DC injection braking. The drive will inject DC into the motor – usually by outputting 0Hz, a kind of frozen three-phase output – and will control the current into the motor. The static magnetic field produced causes an opposing field to be set up by induced currents in the rotor. This produces a braking torque which in practice is OK for low inertia use, but not ever so effective for high inertia loads. It will, however, produce a small holding torque (like a brake) at zero speed, which can sometimes be useful in production applications. DC braking is great for the drive, because no energy comes back to the DC link. The inertial energy from the load is dissipated in the rotor of the motor, so it is possible to overheat the motor if DC braking is continuous. DC braking can usually be set up so it is applied for a certain time following a stop command, and the current level can be adjusted to prevent overheating.
   Some drives offer a mixture of DC braking and ramp down, (a DC offset is applied to the falling frequency) known as compound braking. Like DC, this has limited capability with high inertia loads, but has the added advantage that you know when the motor has stopped, because you have ramped it down.

If none of the above is effective, we must use our braking chopper (or buy an external one if our drive doesn't include one) and a suitable external resistor. The drive can normally regenerate at least its rated current, and the losses work in your favour, so a high braking torque is possible. Now you can get very fast ramp down times as the drive takes the inertial energy onto the DC link, and the chopper then controls the DC link voltage by dumping the energy into the resistor, as described in chapter 5.

Many drives have a programmable duty cycle limitation to protect the resistor from overheating, so this needs setting for your requirements. Otherwise, the chopper takes care of itself, basically controlling the DC link as required. The chopper will usually switch the resistor in and out at a couple of kilohertz, varying the on off times depending on the DC link voltage. For more information about selecting and protecting a braking resistor, see box: **Selecting Braking Resistors**.

Selecting Braking Resistors

You can usually buy braking resistors from the drive supplier, and these may be packaged for convenience, mounting under the drive or next to it. Some drives have small resistors built in. However, these are not low cost solutions, and generally have a limited duty cycle capability. That is, they are designed for full power braking for maybe 10 seconds in 200 – a 5% duty cycle. This is fine if your load is low inertia or if you only brake occasionally. But for higher inertias or duty cycles you must choose your own resistor from another supplier. The ohmic value will determine the peak current in the resistor and the braking chopper IGBT, so don't choose a lower value than the drive manufacturer recommends. The instantaneous power capability of the resistor depends on the DC voltage when regenerating (maybe 15% above the normal DC voltage) and the aforesaid ohmic value. But to correctly size the resistor, we need to know the operating duty cycle. If you are lowering something all the time (a downhill conveyer, a down escalator) then you are generating all the time and you need a 100% rated resistor. But more likely the drive regenerates occasionally during ramp down, and you can calculate the duty cycle accordingly. At this point, it's best to get the supplier of the resistor to do the selection, and then he has to get it right. Specify the requirements along the lines of:
7.5kW drive, lifting 50% 1 minute, lowering 50% 1 minute minimum resistor value 56R, 800V DC working, IP20 (protection level – see chapter 3).
He should sell you a nice 56R resistor about 3kW rated in a finger proof box. Remember if you mount it in your electrical cabinet, you'll warm everything up in there. Stick it on top of the cabinet if it is a fairly clean environment. If in doubt, choose a nice big resistor; they don't cost too much.

Many drives will offer a kinetic buffering or controlled regeneration in the event of a short mains break. If the supply fails, the drive can choose to slow the load down, regenerating just enough to hold the DC link constant, powering the power supply and keeping the drive running. If the mains returns within a few seconds, (depending on the inertia and losses in the load) then the drive will speed up to the setpoint and the process can continue uninterrupted. Handy for high inertia loads.

Stopping and Braking – Conclusions

A little care is needed when setting the deceleration time or deciding on braking methods. Most applications don't need a braking chopper or resistor, either because rapid deceleration isn't needed, or because there are enough losses or load in the system that not enough energy returns to the drive. For those that need some form of braking, resistive braking is the only solution that will absorb a significant amount of energy, and the resistor should be chosen based on some simple calculations.
Like acceleration, deceleration can usually have smoothing added if required, and alternative ramp rates selected in various ways.

Maximum and Minimum Frequencies

Drives are usually supplied with a minimum frequency of 0Hz and a maximum of 50 or 60Hz, depending on the motor frequency. A minimum frequency is often programmed by the user - maybe 10 or 20Hz - when working with centrifugal pumps or fans, as below this frequency they are not very effective. A minimum frequency may also be set for process reasons, or to ensure the drive is stopped, rather than just slowed to 0Hz, with current still flowing in the motor (see later when we talk about boost).
Maximum frequencies are a little harder to deal with. Everyone wants to go faster. Problem is, you'll remember from our discussions about flux that, at higher frequencies the flux and therefore the available torque, reduces. The motors are designed to be at optimum flux at 50Hz 400 or 230V. If the frequency is increased, the flux reduces, because we can't increase the voltage any more. So if you increase the speed of the motor by increasing the output frequency of the drive above nominal, then expect the torque to reduce. This is called field weakening in DC motors, but in AC motors is called flux weakening. Or maybe field weakening as well sometimes. In some applications this loss of torque capability is no problem, but in others the motor will stall.

The other problem is the motor. In general, the motor bearings etc. are probably OK to twice normal speed, but it's worth checking. If you're making a high speed polishing machine, or you want your washing machine to spin at a ridiculous speed for a short time, then a high maximum frequency may be the solution. Up to 300Hz (that's 18,000rpm on a two pole motor) may be OK for a short time.

Of course, if you are enriching Uranium and have a large number of very high-speed centrifuges, a drive and special motor is just what you need (actually hundreds of drives and special motors; if anyone asks why you want them, say it's a textile application), but most applications rarely stray above 100Hz. Nevertheless, drive manufacturers will usually allow the maximum frequency to be set to 500Hz or more.

We'll see later how higher frequencies can get more power from a motor.

Voltage to frequency Modifications

We've mentioned (several times) that, as the frequency is reduced from the motor nominal, we must also reduce the voltage to prevent motor saturation. Theoretically a motor requires a linear relationship between voltage and frequency, but above 50Hz no more voltage is available (as discussed above), and at 0Hz obviously we need more than 0V output from the drive. In theory, a motor can develop full torque at 0Hz but if torque and magnetising current are to flow, we'll need some voltage to overcome the resistances and inductances in the motor. So most drives include a modification to the V to f relationship so that an extra 'boost' voltage is included. The boost voltage is often set to provide enough voltage to supply full load current into the motor's nominal stator resistance at 0Hz. The boost voltage is blended into the linear V to f curve in different ways, some boost remaining right up to 50Hz.

The boost value makes a big difference to the torque at low speed, but an excessive boost can lead to high losses, so the user can usually adjust the boost, say between 0 and 250% of nominal value. The trick is not to overdo the boost as this will saturate the motor and torque will be lost. An addition to 'continuous' boost is to add even more boost at start up, or during acceleration, in order to help with 'sticky' loads like mixers or conveyers. The boost goes back to the continuous level during running to minimise losses and avoid potential overheating.

Different V to f curves can also be selected. Clearly selecting a 60Hz motor will run the curve to 100% at 60Hz instead of 50Hz. A cunning variation on the V to f curve is to use a 400V drive with a motor connected as a 230V motor. This is possible because, as mentioned in chapter 3, many small IEC motors can be connected in delta for 230V operation and star for 400V operation. The power remains the same, and the current goes up or down as expected. Hence the dual ratings on many motor rating plates.

Now if we wire the motor in delta for 230V operation and run it on a 230V 50Hz curve with a 400V drive, all's well because the motor's insulation is designed for 400V operation, so the higher voltage peaks won't harm it. The average 'sine wave' voltage is 230V at 50Hz still. Now if we increase the frequency above 50Hz what happens? We have some spare voltage because this inverter will output 400V, so the frequency rises and so does the voltage, the flux now remains constant so we have full torque capability. In fact, we maintain full torque until the drive output reaches 400V, which happens at about 87Hz (do the sums; it's √3 times 50Hz). Full torque and higher speed means higher power; in fact we have √3 times more power from the motor. Not a bad trick, providing the bearings are up to it (they should be). The drive is fully rated of course. So drives usually include an 87Hz curve among their various V to f settings. Some NEMA motor windings can be configured in series or parallel to do a similar trick with 60Hz 230V or 120Hz 460V. If you are designing a large conveyer system, this can be a neat saving; you just design the gearboxes accordingly. But the downside is you can't easily switch to direct on line operation without reconnecting the motors if a drive fails.

Quadratic V to f Curves

Another variation of V to f curves is offered for use with pumps and fans. Many, but not all, fans and non-reciprocating pumps have a variable torque load characteristic. Basically they do very little work at low speed, the load increasing roughly as the square of the speed. So (the argument goes), the motor doesn't need as much flux at lower speeds, and a reduction in flux will save a little in magnetising current losses. So a V to f curve is offered which follows a parabolic (or roughly parabolic) shape, hopefully giving the right flux level for the load. This option is referred to as the 'quadratic' or 'pump and fan' curve as engineers' imagination runs away again. It's also sometimes called a variable torque load, compared with a constant torque load such as a conveyer. Drive engineers will talk about VT and CT settings just to confuse those not in the know. To confuse things even more, VT and CT have recently been replaced by low overload and high overload - LO and HO, although a lot of people stick to VT and CT. Selecting a VT setting often changes the rating and overload capability of larger drives – see box: **CT and VT Ratings**.

The figure below summarises these V to f variations; boost can be added to all curve variants, but is not shown here.

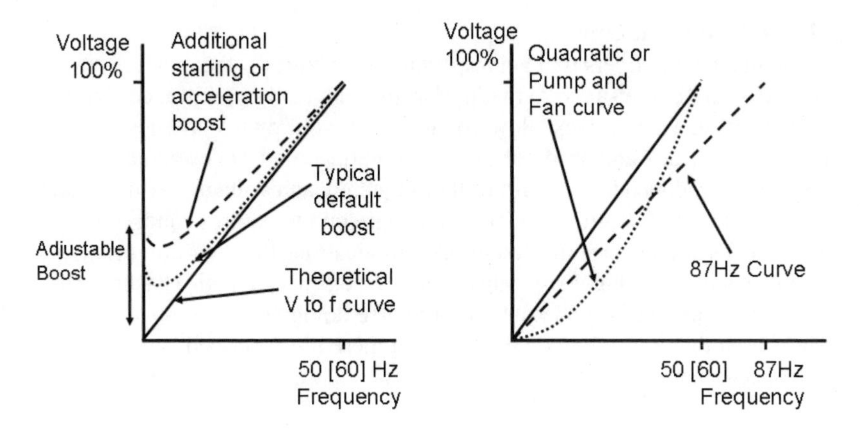

Figure 8.4 Voltage to Frequency Variations

CT and VT Ratings

Drives are designed to be able to provide full torque – that is current - at zero speed, and also provide some overload capability for acceleration or short term loading. This is fine for most loads, but pumps and fans are a bit different. If we discount acceleration loading, pumps and fans rarely run in overload, because the power would rise so much (see chapter 9), or the pump or fan would stall. So the sales guys came up with the idea of reducing the overload capability of the drive a little when it was run with the VT curve, and pushing up the continuous output. The engineers cursed and ran their tests, and found, surprisingly, that with a little tweaking they could get the drive to run the next size up motor, at least for larger drives. The competitive advantage of this was immediately lost as all the drive manufacturers copied this. So now, if you select the VT setting on many drives (typically above 7.5kW), the output capability rises to the next rating, and the overload capability drops. So a 15kW drive becomes 18.5kW, a 37kW turns into a 45kW etc. The marketing guys then went further, and took a standard drive, added some pump friendly features (see chapter 9) set the VT rating as default, changed the colour and offered a 'pump and fan' drive with a bit more output. Fine for pumps and fans, but of course some smart guys bought this cheaper product and put it on conveyers or mixers, and wondered why they wouldn't provide any torque at low speed. The moral is, check your load characteristics carefully before buying the pump and fan drive with the VT setting.

Other V to f Variants

Some machine builders will get a special motor built for them that needs a special V to f curve suited to that motor; this can really optimise cost and performance. Many drives allow you to design your own V to f curve, using lots of parameters and a 'join the dots' technique. You can even take completely independent control of the frequency and voltage, say using one analogue input to control frequency, and a second to control voltage. This allows drives to be used in some wacky applications that don't involve motors such as driving weird transformers or electromagnetic shakers and vibration tables. Hope you know what you're doing here.
There are other control mode variants, but these are described later under Advanced Features.

Warnings and Faults

Most drives have pretty good protection systems built in to stop the drive or the motor, or even the load from being damaged. Limits can be set on current, torque, speed, even power. When these limits are reached, the drive will usually control to the limit, and will indicate a warning, maybe by flashing the display and showing a meaningless number. Many digital outputs are programmed by default to indicate a warning or fault, which is useful for the supervisory system. If the situation is more serious, then the drive may shut down to protect itself or the motor. This will be indicated by a fault, and again a number in the display, and maybe a digital output. The numbers aren't, of course, meaningless; you can look them up in the manual, and the diagnostics may be helpful.

Some Useful Features

So far we've looked at some general settings and functions that you'll probably need in any application. Now let's look at some features that are useful for particular applications.

Automatic Start/Restart

When you power up a drive it will go through some initialisation (hopefully fairly quickly) and it will then wait for a command – probably to run. Even if you have programmed the digital inputs to be level sensitive, it will still look for a change of state before starting. This is a sensible safety measure, as you don't normally want the drive to start when the power comes back after a mains break unless you toggle the run/stop.

However, if you have a remote installation you don't want to send a service guy out in the middle of the night following a power cut to restart the drive. Similarly, some machines should start when the power is applied. So it is possible to programme drives to start when the power is applied, or following a trip for example. You can even programme the drive to try to start a number of times following a fault, but after ten tries something is probably dead, so it's a good time to stop – and they do. Auto restart is a useful feature, but should be selected with care.

Flying Restart

We normally expect to start a drive from 0Hz on a stopped motor. However, in some applications the motor is already rotating. Maybe there was a short mains break on a high inertia machine and we are using Auto restart. Maybe a fan is spinning slowly in the draught of an air conditioning system. It may even be spinning backwards, depending on the ducting layout. If we start our drive on the rotating motor, it may trip on overcurrent, or if we are lucky, jerk into life and start ramping to the setpoint.

If we enable the flying restart, or spin start function, then the drive will be a little more circumspect at start up. Usually it will run low voltage sweep between maximum and minimum frequencies and look for the minimum current. This will be around about the motor speed; knowing this, it will start from there and ramp the motor up or down to the setpoint as normal. With a little variation it can sweep in reverse as well if we expect the motor to be running backwards, like our fan feeding the ducts. The drive will then take the fan back to zero and then forwards to the setpoint. A word of caution here. Flying restart will energise the motor during its sweep, and if the motor is stopped, not rotating, on some drives it may move it a little, forwards and backwards if it is looking in both directions. On a fan this is no problem, but some machines object expensively to going backwards. So don't switch on flying restart unless you need it, and disable the 'check in both directions' function if applicable.

Skip or Resonant Frequencies

Resonance is a blessing or a curse, depending on what you are doing. In many applications it is undesirable to run a motor at a particular speed or frequency because the resulting vibration or noise could damage equipment. In air conditioning systems, ducting and fan blades can resonate to create disturbing noises. The answer is to set a skip frequency.

The drive will avoid this frequency, and a couple of Hertz either side of it, even if the control system demands it. It will ramp through as normal. One or more skip frequencies can be programmed on most drives.

Brake control

Mechanical brakes are sometimes needed for safety or operational reasons. Electrically operated brakes can be specified on motors. For safety reasons, when the electromagnet is energised the brake is released; power failure or a break in the wiring will bring the brake on. The usual technique here is to release (i.e. energise) the brake a short time after the drive has started and reached a minimum frequency. This allows the flux and torque to build in the motor, so the load is taken up fairly smoothly. Similarly, when a stop command is given, the drive will ramp down and the brake will come on at a minimum frequency and, after a short delay, the drive is shut off. This, or similar sequencing, is looked after by the drive and a couple of user settings. By the way, if you are switching a highly inductive load like a brake coil make sure you use the digital output to control some beefy contactor rather than switch it directly from the tiny relay in the drive.

Slip Compensation

Here's a neat idea. You'll recall the induction motor doesn't quite run at the speed related to the frequency (it is an **a**synchronous motor) it lags this by the slip frequency. Now the slip is pretty much proportional to the load, and we can get a rough idea of the load from the current, which we are measuring as well as we can afford. So we can boost the output frequency by a little, based again on our knowledge of the motor type and load current, to compensate for the change in speed due to slip. This is a fairly easy, safe adjustment to make, and the user can trim the amount of adjustment to give pretty good speed holding over a range of frequencies. This is handy with a conveyer for example, where we want the speed to be pretty constant whatever the load. Slip compensation can create positive feedback; that is, if the drive over compensates and takes on more load because the speed actually increases, it will pile on more slip compensation and more load will follow. The answer, as always, is apply with care.

Simple Positioning, or 'Controlled Stop'

This is a variation on a ramp down. If you've set a ramp down time of say 10 seconds, related to 50Hz, then the stopping times, and more importantly, the stopping number of revolutions (or distance on a conveyer) will be dependent on the speed the motor is going at when the stop (or strictly speaking 'Ramp down and Stop') command is given.

So if the drive is running at 25Hz, the stop time will be 5 seconds, but from 5Hz it will only be one second. The stopping distance will vary greatly. For a fan this doesn't matter, but if you want to position a pizza to add the topping, it can make life difficult. Many users here will use one sensor to detect the pizza, slow the pizza-carrying conveyer to a crawl, and then stop when a second sensor says so. A neater solution is to use this simple positioning feature, which calculates a ramp down time so that, following a stop command from the sensor, the drive always stops in the same number of revolutions, irrespective of the speed. This not only saves a sensor, but also speeds up production. These options are shown in the figure below. And yes, drives are used in pizza manufacturing, see chapter 9.

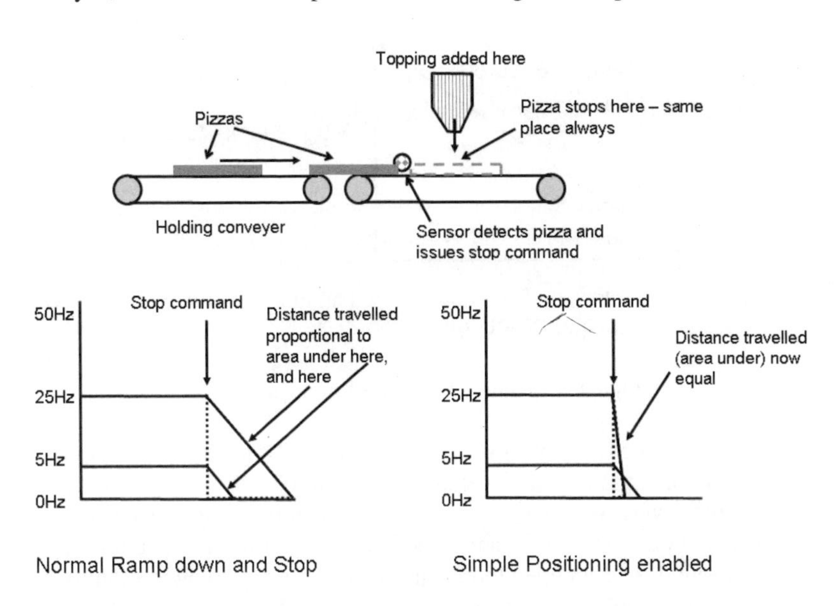

Figure 8.5 Pizza topping and Simple Positioning

Current Limit and Torque Control

So far we've talked about controlling and monitoring the current mainly in order to protect the drive and motor from the overall magnitude of the current, or possibly calculate heating effects in the motor. However, many applications find it useful to control, monitor or limit the torque produced by the motor, as described in chapter 6. In a DC motor, the armature current is pretty closely related to the torque, so torque control is pretty easy with a DC machine.

However, with an AC machine, we need to get an idea of how much of the overall current produces torque, and how much produces flux – that is, the magnetising current. We can separate the two fairly easily in theory; after all, the torque producing current is pretty much resistive, and the magnetising current is pretty much inductive. As long as we know the phase angle relative to the voltage (and we should do, we're generating the voltage using PWM), we can solve the triangle shown in the figure below. For various reasons, it's not always that easy, particularly at low frequencies, but reasonably good torque figures can be calculated on this basis.

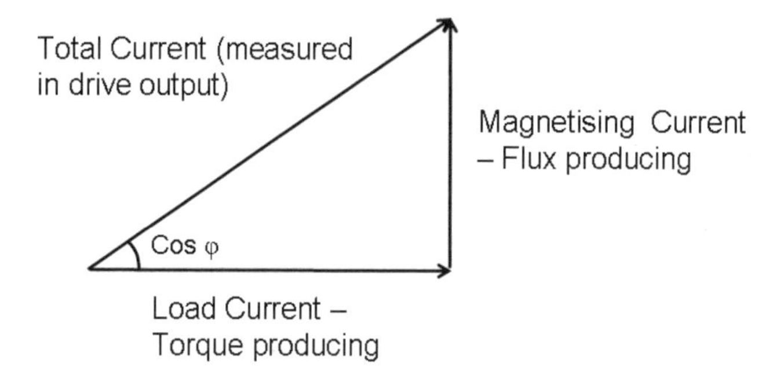

Figure 8.6 Magnetising and Load Currents

Now we can decide if we want to control the *overall current* for motor or drive protection, or the *torque current* if we want to control torque in the process. Either way, we are now in closed loop control. Before, we had generated an output frequency and hoped that the motor runs at about the desired speed; that is, an open loop control. Now we are going to monitor the current (either all, or just the torque part) and adjust the output frequency to keep it (the current) constant, reduce it or whatever. So we have to think about gain terms, stability etc, and described in chapter 6.

For torque control or current limiting, you'll find various parameters that can be adjusted to improve the system response and stability. In practice, this isn't as difficult as setting, say a temperature controller as the motor current is closely related to the drive, and there aren't unpredictable lags and effects in the system. The default settings for gain and integral terms are probably OK, at least for current limiting.

If we do overload, and the current limit kicks in, the drive will probably react by bringing the output frequency down in an attempt to reduce the current. Remember, if we run the drive in torque control (or continuous current limit for that matter) we are not able to control the output frequency. You can control one or the other. So when you use torque control it is important also to set a frequency limit on your system. Remember the speed and torque servos on the paper machine described in chapter 6? Same thing here with torque and frequency control, only the frequency control is open loop here.

Torque monitoring

If we have a load that is predictable, we can monitor the torque at a particular speed and decide if all is well. For example, a fan will have a low load at low speed, the load - that is, the torque – increasing roughly as the square of the speed. If a belt drives the fan, (a variable torque load) then we can detect if the belt is slipping or snapped because the load will be low at high speeds. We can now programme a digital output to raise a warning or alarm. This is quite useful, because in big air handling systems you want to avoid the expense of additional sensors (to detect air flow or lack of it) for your building management system, and for the drive it's just a bit more software…

Advanced Features

As mentioned earlier, more and more features and functions are added to the simplest of drives to meet more and more users' needs. The following features are rarely used, but when they are, the users are so highly impressed they probably remain loyal to the drive supplier who thought it up, at least until the feature is copied and improved by a competitor.

Interconnection of Functions.
When you want to set up, say, a digital output function – maybe a relay – to tell you the drive has tripped, you go to the handbook and you'll see a list of settings like:

Parameter 999: Relay 1
1. No function
2. Drive Fault
3. Drive running
4. Maximum speed reached
5. Etc.

Set the parameter to '2', and you've programmed the relay to do what you want. Inside the drive, the software does something like "2 means output 14 [relay one driver] is true if drive status word 1 bit 15 [drive tripped] is true". Obviously there are many connection possibilities within the drive. The software structure uses control and status words to store information about what is happening in the drive and its inputs and outputs, but only the connections between those that are most common are listed in the handbook. The others are theoretically possible, but not listed. Perhaps a good example is connecting the spare digital outputs (relays if you are lucky) to spare digital inputs. You'd maybe do this by connecting the relay parameter to a digital input status bit in a digital input status word. Now the user can 'borrow' the relays and use them for other purposes, controlling them via spare digital inputs. Or maybe you want to set up one of the built in push buttons to add another 10Hz to the speed just while it is pressed.

Take the relevant bit from the status word of the push buttons and connect it to a 10Hz fixed frequency. Maybe it needs a couple of other tweaks (like enabling the addition of analogue and fixed frequency setpoints for example), but allowing the user access to the *internal* connections can improve the flexibility of a drive without adding to the cost. Of course, then we get "Wouldn't it be nice to have a timer built in?" Suddenly we have some logic gates, flip-flops, some timers, some arithmetic blocks and comparators. We can start manipulating our inputs and outputs and do some really clever stuff. For example, suppose we have a motor driving rotary cutters that chew up waste material for recycling. Occasionally it overloads and jams when an old tyre comes along. We can detect the overload and trip the drive, and then the operator has to come along, reset it, reverse the drive and maybe try again to get the tyre through.

With the function blocks provided, we can monitor the motor current (or torque) and, using a comparator, detect a high load. If we stop the drive, reverse it for a time (using a flip-flop and timer maybe) then restart it, maybe we can clear the overload automatically. It takes a bit of programming, but if you build these machines (as they do in South America) getting the drive to do the work instead of using an external controller (PLC or man) is a significant saving.

So that's a brief introduction to internal connections and function blocks; you can see this kind of stuff can just keep expanding, and some drives offer near PLC like capability. However, the cost is more software complexity, more complex documentation, and greater demands on customer support systems. Many users long for a drive with a Run/stop and 0 – 10V speed control and nothing else.

Parameter sets

Many drives offer the ability to programme different sets of parameters and change between them. This allows the user to completely change the function of the drive by switching from one active set to another. You may want to use the drive on two different motors, say one that lifts and one that traverses. Easy. Programme the first parameter set for the lifting motor, say 11kW with high boost and slow ramp rates. The second parameter set is programmed for the 5.5kW traverse motor with fast ramp rates. Of course, you can't use both at the same time, and you need some careful interlocking when you switch parameter sets and the drive output between motors, but it saves a drive. Also useful for changing from manual operation (analogue setpoint, slow ramps, open loop) to automatic operation (setpoint from serial interface, fast ramps, closed loop). Some drives allow several control parameter sets, or several motor parameter sets; it can get a bit complicated – you need to be sure you don't disable the function of the parameter set select switch when you switch parameters, or you're really in trouble....

Closed Loop (PID) Control

We've already discussed closed loop control systems for controlling stuff inside the drive as well as outside, such as pressure, temperature or flow rate. Now we have to think about setting this up. Suppose we want to maintain a constant water pressure in a building. We'll monitor the pressure at a suitable point, and feed the signal from the transducer back to the drive. Hopefully we have a 0 – 10V signal or something similar, so we'll use an analogue input. This means we either need another analogue input for the setpoint, or the setpoint comes from a fixed value or via a serial link. The setpoint is no longer a frequency. It's now some pressure value, like psi or Pascals or something; the drive will be happy to work in percentages now.

So we have a setpoint and an actual (feedback) value, we can now enable our closed loop controller, which will look very like the one described in chapter 6, but instead of preset pots you'll have parameter values to adjust. With a bit of care the system can be stabilised by tweaking the P, I, and (not so often) D settings, and the drive will then continually adjust the speed of the pump to maintain constant pressure as demand varies. The trick with closed loop systems like this is to make sure the feedback signal (in this case from the pressure transducer) is properly scaled and signed to suit the drive. Most drives allow the analogue input to be scaled (say 2.5 – 5V) to match the transducer signal. Incidentally, your signal may go the opposite way to the motor speed, then you'll need to invert it, also possible by setting a parameter. For example, if you run a cooling system, and the transducer gives 0 – 10V for 0 – 50° C say, then speeding up the motor will give more cooling and reduce the feedback signal. You won't stabilise this unless you change the sense of the signal by changing the 'transducer type' or 'transducer sense' parameter, so the feedback and setpoint are in the same sense.

Some control systems work better if the range of adjustment is limited. In this case the closed loop will only trim the speed say +/- 10% around the setpoint. This is called a (wait for it) trim function, and is often used for tension control in winding applications (see chapter 9).
There are plenty of other adjustments and parameters in a closed loop control system, and some drives offer 'Auto set up' features to help tuning. Auto set up routines often use the Ziegler–Nichols tuning method, which I've mentioned just for the name.
Closed loop control can get complicated, so start off with something simple.

Flux Current Control, Vector Control and Marketing

It is the goal of the drives designer to ensure the customer has the maximum possible torque available at all output frequencies, and the highest efficiency drive and motor system. Getting the flux level right is critical for this, and we've seen this can be tricky, particularly at low frequencies. Various techniques are used to overcome this. As stated earlier, a DC machine has separate windings for field and armature, but in an AC motor they are all lumped together. If we can separate the load current and magnetising current as described earlier, then knowing what the magnetising current should be (we know the motor type and size from the nameplate data that was loaded into the drive) we can estimate and adjust the magnetising current by varying the voltage a little way from the V to f curve. Although this is pretty crude, it can give some improvement over the V to f curve, which is, after all, a 'one size fits all' solution. This minor adjustment can be called Flux Current Control (FCC), or many similar variations to give the idea of improved performance. One advantage with FCC is that it doesn't require any special setting up, so is ideal for a simple, standard drive.

However, if we want better performance, we need to analyse more carefully what the motor is doing, which brings us to Vector Control (VC). The reason it's called vector control is that it tries to control the flux and everything else as vector quantities not scalar quantities. Huh? Put another way, the drive tries to give the required voltage depending on the exact state of the motor, including the rotor *position*. If you know the rotor position and the currents in the stator, you can work out what is happening in terms of flux, torque and speed pretty easily. You can then apply the necessary pulse widths to the relevant stator winding, bearing in mind the rotor position; you are controlling the flux *vector* – i.e. value plus angle, of the flux or whatever. Anything else is just FCC or a variation of it.

If you have an encoder fitted this isn't too difficult as you have speed feedback (see later), and you can (probably) calculate the rotor position from this. Now with a sufficiently good motor equivalent circuit model in the drive, you can really get the flux right and give maximum torque capability, even at zero speed. This is the best way to do cranes and lifts, where the last thing you want when starting off is to get the torque wrong and drop the load.

But if you don't have an encoder, things can be tricky. As the doors close on the lift and the brake comes off, you don't know if the motor is just holding the load, jerking the single passenger up, or dropping a fully loaded cage down. However, theoretically, if you have a perfect mathematical model of the motor, you *can* predict what is happening, especially if you have very accurate current (and maybe voltage) measurement and you can then apply your vector control as with an encoder. Trouble is, to get the model right you need a lot of accurate information about the motor. The user needs to give this to the drive, and even then there are challenges. For example, the characteristics of the motor (especially the stator resistance) change with temperature, so you either need feedback of the motor temperature, or you need a really good thermal model. Some motors now include a linear temperature sensor, as opposed to a simple over temperature detector, to help with this. However, if you are working with just a thermal model, what happens if the drive is switched off and then on again? Do you 'forget' the motor temperature? What about when the ambient is high? All these things make VC without an encoder (often called Sensorless Vector Control – SVC, or even SLVC) quite difficult. With high speed processing and some pretty good mathematical models, as well as better current measurement methods, things have got better, but I have yet to meet a SVC designer who will stand under a 16 ton weight suspended from a crane when the 'run real slow' command is given and the brake released. Vector Control has certainly made performance improvements at higher speeds, but full torque at zero speed is still difficult to achieve. If you want to try it on a simple drive, take care setting the drive up with the correct motor information; test it carefully hot and cold before shipping it to China. Or maybe you want a trip to China...

Marketing and other Hype

So why bring up marketing here? Well, FCC, VC, SVC are all used and distorted to help sell drives. Not everyone wants to use a drive on a lift or crane, but the marketing guys will try to convince you that you need this high level of performance on your fan, pump or conveyer system. There are many different names now used (like Voltage Vector Control and Flux Vector Control) to describe what is anything from a slightly tweaked V to f curve controller to a full-blown Vector control. So most users can't tell which suppliers have good designers and which have good Marketing departments. Just as a car salesman will talk about Active Steering Control or something else in capital letters, the drives supplier will have something equally baffling, but usually with the word Vector included.

My advice here is, if you don't need it, don't pay for it or try to use it. If you do need it on your crane or lift, you'll need to do a lot of careful analysis in any case to get it right, so involve the drive supplier from day one and make sure you understand what's going on. You'll probably end up with an encoder…

Encoders and Speed Feedback

We've mentioned above that an encoder will really help when using Vector Control, but of course its real purpose is to measure the speed of the motor to give accurate speed holding via a closed loop system. This is needed less of the time than you might think, especially for simple drives. As stated earlier, most users aren't interested in the motor speed at all, they are much more interested in the pressure or temperature, the steady flow of bottles into the capping machine, the diversion of luggage to this or that aircraft. So most speed control is indirect, a supervisory controller somewhere telling the dumb drive to speed up or down. However, if you do want accurate speed control, or even position control, you'll need an encoder. These can be factory fitted or you can put them on yourself (they fit on the back of the motor), but alignment is critical as any 'wobble' on the encoder will upset the control system.

Encoders come in different types, but they all use a rotating, slotted disc that interrupts the light between an LED and optical sensor, so a series of pulses are produced proportional to speed. A good encoder will have at least 500 slots per revolution; 1024 seems a common number. In order to give an indication of direction, a second series of slots is often provided, slightly offset from the first set, and many encoders include a third, single slot which can be used for positioning, if you count the pulses correctly. The figure below shows how the pulses are generated and how the phasing between the pulse trains indicates direction.

So an encoder interface on the drive needs to read the pulses (sometimes the signals are differential, A and $\bar{A}$ for example) and maybe supply the encoder, usually with 24V. Programme the drive with the encoder pulses per revolution, and then it's just a question of tuning the speed loop.

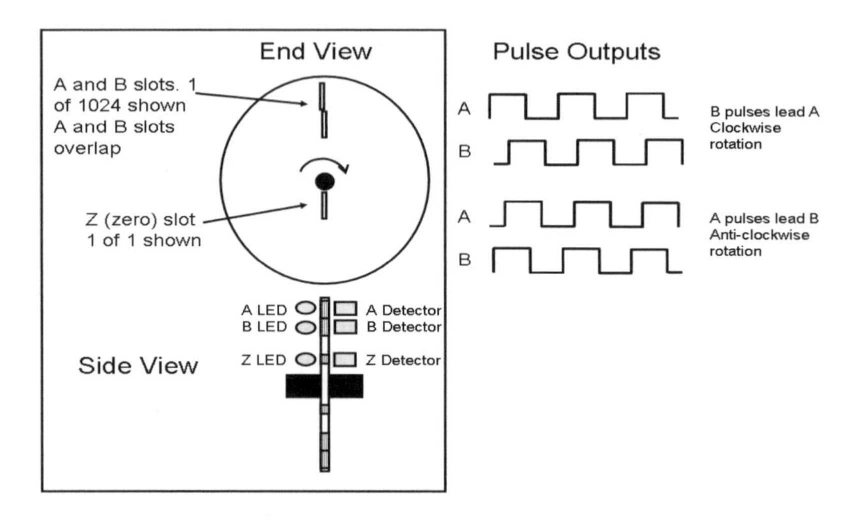

Figure 8.7 Encoders and Encoder Signals

Encoders are mounted on the motor, so it is usual to route the encoder cable in the same duct at the motor cable. This can lead to all sorts of interference problems (see chapter 10); at least use screened cable please.

Serial Communications

Of course, an increasing number of drives are controlled using serial communications. Drives can now be programmed, re-programmed, controlled and monitored using a serial link to a PLC or similar industrial controller. The bits and bytes of this are a bit beyond this book, but of course the correct settings are needed for the drive to accept control from the interface, so some basic parameters must be set on the drive itself.

If you want to use serial communications, note the following:

- For communication to work at all the correct baud rate must be set and a suitable address assigned to the drive. (Some systems will test all possible addresses and baud rates to find drives on the bus)
- The drive and controller must be correctly connected together. Many serial interfaces use the RS485 hardware protocol, which is essentially a two wire plus 0V system, and is designed for industrial applications – See chapter 6.
- Most manufacturers will offer a simple control system using their own protocol. This will make control from a PC easy, provided you have loaded their software onto the PC. However, it won't communicate so easily with other equipment such as PLCs from other manufacturers, but it offers a neat, low cost solution in a small machine for example.
- For larger, factory wide systems, a better solution is to use an *open fieldbus* to control your drive and system. These are internationally defined bus systems that enable different manufacturers' products to operate on a common bus. Ethernet does this for PCs and the Internet. For industrial systems, there are several fieldbus systems, notably Profibus (and derivatives such as Profinet, Profisafe) Canbus, Devicenet, Modbus etc. To interface to these, most drives manufacturers offer optional interface modules for their drives.

These days about 30% of drives are sold with some form of fieldbus option, so the trend is clearly for this style of automation.

Features for Pumps and Fans

As mentioned earlier, the marketing guys may well offer a 'pump and fan' drive to try to get a slice of that highly competitive market. As well as pumping the power up a little, they'll ask the software engineers to add some features (at no extra cost of course). These may or may not be included in the standard product (product differentiation and all that). Typical features are:

Shut off, or Hibernation

This is a simple idea. If the drive is operating with an external closed loop control, say controlling water pressure in a building, then if the demand falls to zero (in an office block at night maybe, unless the software engineers are working late) the drive will reduce the pump speed to zero, or minimum speed. We've seen before that, even at zero speed, the motor will still draw current, so hibernation mode will shut off the drive completely under these conditions, and wait for the demand to come back up before restarting.

Bypass Control

This is pretty popular for pumps and fans. The drive can be programmed to control contactors, via its digital outputs, that will switch the drive out of circuit and run the motor direct on line. Why? Well, you may decide you want to save the drive losses if you are running at full speed (i.e. 50Hz) all the time. Or you may just be using the drive as a soft start to run the motor up to speed. Or possibly you are concerned that the drive might fail (as if!) and running the motor at fixed speed is better than nothing at all. Setting up bypass is a bit hairy as you really want to avoid getting the contactor sequence wrong and connecting mains to the drive output (a good way to break the drive).

Staging

We use the digital outputs again here, but now the idea is to switch in and out additional pumps (or whatever) to support high demand. So you run your drive, motor and pump to maintain, say flow rate into an football stadium, using the closed loop control as before. At half time everyone goes and 'washes their hands', and demand soars. The pump speeds up to maximum. And cannot provide enough flow. Luckily you've thought of this, so you have a second, fixed speed motor and pump, that the drive now switches on. The drive even slows down to accommodate the second pump coming in, and controls flow rate as before. If demand rises still further (at full time everyone goes to the washroom again, and the teams have showers) the drive will demand more flow, hit maximum, and switch in another fixed speed pump, and another if needed. As demand reduces, the fixed speed pumps are switched off, the variable speed pump adjusting its speed accordingly. It takes some setting up, but this actually works rather well.

Summary

You can keep adding features and functions to drives until you run out of memory or software engineers, but the trick is always to supply stuff that is useful to the user, easy to set up and use, and doesn't over complicate the drive. This is not easy to do if we are limited on cost for, say, the display or interface. Let's look at some applications and see where the drives and their features really get used.

9. Applications of AC Drives

So we now have a basic understanding of how an AC drive is put together, and how the software enables a whole host of features and functions to be included in the product; but where are the drives used?
Horse exercising machines, hot tub pumps and rotating stages in dubious clubs are some of the more unusual uses, but this doesn't account for the several million drives that are sold every year. In this chapter we'll look at some of the more common applications, again focussing on the simpler uses for drives, rather than describing a five colour printer and its high performance servo systems. Let's start with the most popular and work through.

Fans and pumps

For reasons we'll see below, fans and pumps are lumped together and represent about half of the market for AC drives. Flow, pressure and temperature can all be regulated by controlling the speeds of fans and pumps, so the improved control offered by drives is a clear advantage here. We've already mentioned some of the difficulties of starting and stopping high inertia loads like fans. Direct on line starting of pumps can apply shock through piping systems that can damage them. But a compelling reason for using a drive with either a pump or fan is to save money; or more precisely, energy.
If we ignore pumps or compressors (see later) that use positive displacement to move fluid – like a piston pump for example – then the majority of fans and pumps consume power proportional to the cube of their speed. Why? Well, we start with Bernoulli's equation (Bernoulli was an 18th century Dutch Swiss mathematician):

$$P + \rho \cdot v^2/2 = \text{Constant}$$

Where P is pressure, ρ is the density of the fluid, and v is its velocity. For a fan or pump, the flow rate is generally proportional to the speed of the fan or pump. The more fluid you move against the pressure, the more power you'll need, so power is proportional to flow rate x pressure. But Bernoulli tells us pressure is proportional to $(\text{flow rate})^2$, which means power is proportional to $(\text{flow rate})^3$, which is the relationship we wanted to help sell the drive in the first place.

From Bernoulli's equation we can calculate the energy in a dam, or the changes in pressure and flow rate as we pass fluids through different diameter piping. We can calculate the power required to fill a tank at a particular height (i.e. pressure) at a particular flow rate. Or we can work out the power needed to move a certain amount of air against a static pressure. A ducting engineer can convert all his flows to equivalent pressure drops, add them up and select the necessary fan.
This cube law relationship means that these applications work with drives in variable torque setting, hence the 'pump and fan' drives described earlier (see chapter 8).

So how about energy saving, key to selling our drives? Well, reduce fan or pump speed by 20% from, say, 50 to 40Hz, and power falls to 0.8^3, which is about 52% power, or almost half, as a drive salesman would say.
Can we really save money with a drive? See box: **A Real Example**.

A Real Example

A bus depot has a large extractor fan on the roof, 75kW – a bit bigger than the one in your bathroom. The purpose is to extract the diesel fumes from the bus depot to keep the drivers fit and healthy. The fan was selected for worst case operation, which is maybe Monday morning when all the engines have started, and the drivers are ironically out the back having a cigarette. But once the buses have set off, we can reduce the fan speed, and if we're really clever, use a sensor to measure the noxious content of the air, and use the closed loop control in the drive to maintain a safe level. As I said, this is a real example (except the bit about the cigarettes. – I made that up). The gain? Well, a drive this size will cost a few thousand pounds by the time you'll installed and commissioned it. Suppose we were running the fan 12 hours a day, and electricity costs 5p/kWh (less than I pay). Total cost over 250 days (a year if you don't run buses or fan at the weekend) £11,250. If, with the drive fitted, we save half the power, I reckon the payback is less than a year, and you're reducing wear, noise and your carbon footprint as well. In many cases it really is that simple. OK, realistically, there will be a few more losses with a drive fitted and we've assumed the motor is 100% efficient, but you get the picture, and that is only slowing the fan a little. During the rush hour when all the buses are on the road (well, let's make the assumption at least) we can slow the fan right down or stop it entirely (using hibernation mode; see chapter 8).

Fans

So what other applications are there with fans with drives? Well, engineers like initials and catch phrases, so here's another one: Heating, Ventilating and Air Conditioning: HVAC. Nearly all large buildings now have sophisticated HVAC systems, with large ducts feeding cooling or heating air around. The whole lot is usually controlled by a building management system (shortened to BMS of course) and to give the best climate control variable speed fans are the obvious solution. The system will have been designed for the worst case – the hottest day, maximum capacity, so most of the time less airflow is needed. In the past, the flow rate was controlled by large flaps or dampers, but these saved very little, if any energy, and needed their own motors and systems. These days selling drives to building consultant engineers is easy, especially with the ever-increasing cost of energy. What's difficult is getting them to by your drive, as this is a highly competitive business.

So, buildings, factories, shopping centres, offices, cruise ships – all these places need a controlled environment, and a large system like a shopping centre can easily have twenty or thirty 55kW drives just for air movement. Good business. In many of these applications the reduction in speed and absence of flaps or dampers reduces the noise, which is important in concert halls, depending on the band of course.

If your process requires cleaned and filtered air, you'll have something similar to a BMS system, again with lots of drives. A good example is the 'clean room' used in semiconductor manufacture, where vast amounts of air are controlled and filtered.

Fans aren't only used in HVAC. They are also important for controlling any combustion process. A fire is controllable and more efficient when the inlet and exhaust draughts are assisted with a fan, and of course controlling the airflow is easier with a variable speed drive. Combustion can, of course, be taking place in a power station, a waste processing plant, a glass or steel works or many other manufacturing processes. The same rules of variable torque and consequent energy saving apply, and better control of the combustion is another key advantage of using a variable speed drive here. Again, the old systems of flaps or dampers give limited control and little energy saving.

Getting things hot is one thing, cooling them is just as important. High power fans are used to cool industrial processes directly, or to cool heat exchangers. All sorts of things have to be cooled before packing or further processing, and a drive with a control system will ensure the right temperature is attained. If you want really cold really quickly, then blasting very cold air over fish fingers or peas will freeze them safely and efficiently. In larger applications, heat exchangers a bit like big car radiators usually have large fans either sucking or blowing air over them. These are often referred to as induced draught (ID – sucking) or forced draught (FD - blowing) fans, and each approach has different advantages. A large power station will have fans of hundreds of kilowatts either cooling banks of radiators, or, more usually, large cooling towers with fans at the bottom. The applications continue. Extraction fans take away nasty gases; in wood processing the sawdust is sucked away, and there is quite a science in ensuring the air velocity is maintained so the sawdust doesn't settle in the ducts. Extraction fans are important in tunnels, where the motors are often designed to continue to operate in the event of a fire, taking the smoke away. Smoke extraction motors are also used in buildings for the same reason.

By the way, fans pretty much fall into two types if we discount high pressure blowers and compressors. The common or garden extraction fan is an axial fan, where the air or gas is accelerated parallel to the axis by the propeller like blades. These are good for low pressure, high flow rate systems such as HVAC, cooling heat exchangers etc. Centrifugal fans accelerate the air from the centre of the fan in a circular motion. The air is driven outwards by centrifugal force and is ducted away, new air entering at the centre. It's clearer in the diagram below.

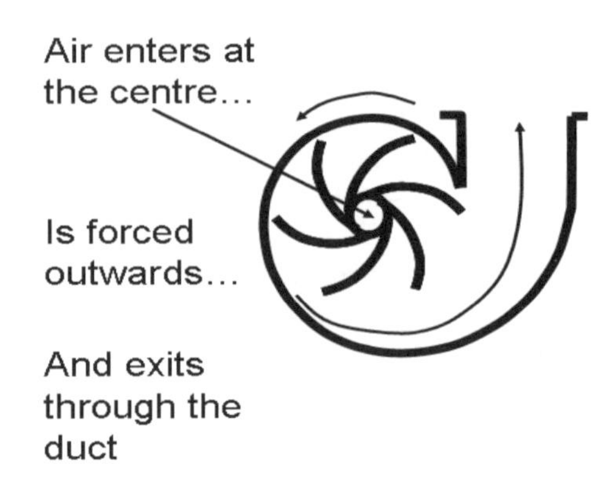

Figure 9.1 Centrifugal Fan

Centrifugal fans tend to produce higher pressures, so are great for furnace fans, large ventilation systems, specialist cooling systems etc.

Figure 9.2 Centrifugal Fans

So fans are a key drive application because of the simplified control, the reduction in stops and starts, reduced noise etc, but the big advantage is certainly the energy saving. The same applies to the other half of the couple, pumps.

Pumps

Pumps are not quite so straightforward. For a start, there are many different types of pumps, and there are many different fluids that are pumped, not to mention mixtures of liquids and solids. Waste water engineers have a whole technology around the problems of cotton buds and other things they have to deal with.

We can separate pumps into positive displacement pumps and others. In a positive displacement pump, the fluid is trapped in a closed chamber before being pushed out. A simple piston pump is the best known example, but there are many different types, including the progressive cavity pump that takes some working out. The figure below shows some of these types.

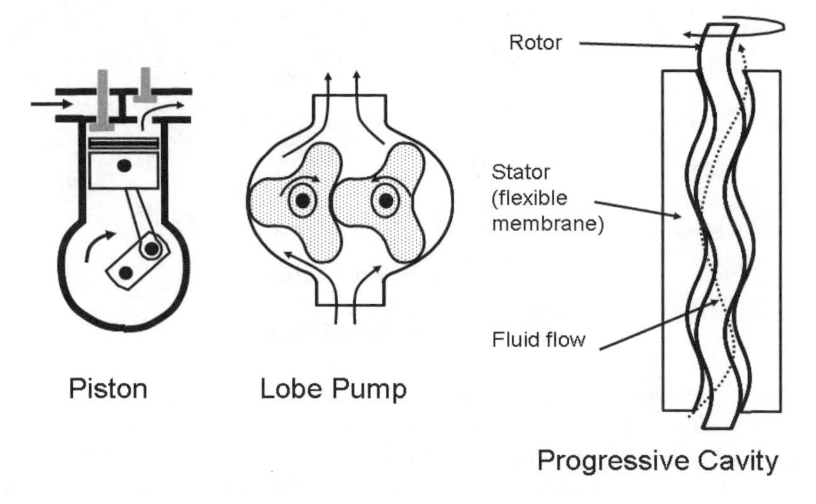

Figure 9.3 Positive displacement Pumps

Positive displacement pumps are used either where precise volume control is needed, or where high pressures are required. Positive displacement pumps basically have a constant torque characteristic.

However, many pumps are centrifugal types, similar in principle to the fans described earlier. These pumps have the same variable torque characteristics as the fans, and consequently show the same energy saving possibilities with drives.

So where are pumps used? Again, this is big business with pumps appearing in nearly all industries. Perhaps the most obvious example for most of us is the distribution of fresh water, and the removal and processing of waste water. In most countries this is a large industry and consumes two or three percent of generated electricity, mostly controlling pumps. Centrifugal pumps are generally used for pumping water, and a typical small installation of two pumps is shown in the figure below. A pump impeller is also shown, and the entry (at the centre) and exit path (at the rim) for the fluid is evident.

Figure 9.4 Centrifugal Pumps

Fresh water used to be fed to towns and cities by gravity alone; the Romans were great at that, but now a complex arrangement of pumps keeps a reasonably constant pressure of water for the domestic and industrial consumer. High power pumps (up to 500kW and more) feed from reservoirs to large cities, while smaller pumps distribute to different areas. Unmanned pumping stations with telemetry are the norm, so a drive on each motor is a natural part of the automation process. Large buildings require their own control and distribution systems, with a small pump maintaining pressure on the upper floors. A drive controlling the pump can slow the pump at night when demand is low, speeding up at breakfast time without the noisy effects of a fixed speed motor stopping and starting. In a small installation the pressure sensor can be connected directly to the drive and the internal closed loop control will do the rest.

Waste water is a bit more involved. The sewage system needs pumps that will tolerate mixtures of solids that we don't want to think about, but must deal with all the same. Raw sewage is pumped to a treatment works, where motors drive filter screens, stirring systems, aeration blowers etc. along with Archimedean screws used for sludge removal etc. Again, automation has ensured drives are an integral part of these systems. The treated water is then suitable for putting back in the river for drinking again. Something else we don't like to think about. Incidentally, one of the by-products of water treatment is a poisonous gas, Hydrogen Sulphide, although it can't be that poisonous as they used to make stink bombs out of it. Hydrogen Sulphide attacks copper to form Copper Sulphide, so any unplated copper in a drive turns black, and busbars (used in larger drives for internal connections) shed flakes of the stuff, leading sooner or later to drive failure. Many, but not all drive manufacturers plate their busbars to prevent this. Worth taking the cover off next time you visit your water treatment works. Both fresh water and waste water pumping stations can be pretty remote, and this can bring special supply problems. If you have a large pumping station in the middle of nowhere, you'd better look closely at the voltage distortion the drives are causing, or you may upset the local farmer's television (see chapter 10).

You may well need a generator for when the mains supply fails, and running drives on generators needs a little care. Water authorities are pretty good with these things now, and spare no expense to ensure system reliability. Water and waste water are big business, but there's a host of other applications for pumps. Let's look at some different industries:

Oil and Gas

Oil often comes out the ground under pressure, but the familiar 'horse head' or 'nodding donkey' pumps are used for shallow low pressure extraction. Powering these with an electric motor and drive can make a significant energy saving compared with a diesel or petrol engine. Perhaps more importantly, maintenance is reduced and reliability increased. If you run a drive in Torque control rather than frequency control, then you can speed up the pump a little on the down stroke, and pump a bit faster – oil men love that. New pumps can be of the progressive cavity types, which are much more compact and better suited to electric drives. Again, remote monitoring, automated control are easier with a drive. Automatic restart (see chapter 8) is essential so the system restarts after a power outage, although a PLC will probably take care of that.

Pumping oil (and compressing gas) along pipelines is increasingly done by motors and drives, replacing gas turbines, but these tend to be very large drives.
In the refinery there's a lot of pumping going on; this is a carefully regulated industry with many safety regulations and when drives are used they must be housed in separate, safe areas.

Heavy Industries

Steel manufacture and metal refining require large amounts of cooling water, which is often sprayed at high pressure onto the hot metal. Coal and minerals require washing and separating. Power stations need pumps for cooling water, turbine lubrication and everything in between. Heavy industries tend to use large high power pumps that run continuously, so energy saving is important.
Smaller dosing pumps are used to add or mix chemicals; here controlling the speed controls the dosage.

Food and Beverage

Process control offers the greatest benefit in 'food and bev'. Bottling beer at high speed requires very careful pressure and flow control to prevent foaming, and the bottles must be pressure washed beforehand if they are 'returns'.
A surprising number of foods are pumped. Specialised 'sanitary' pumps (that is, pumps that handle food) will pump sauces, corn syrup, dough, chocolate as well as non foodstuffs like toothpaste and shampoo. Sanitary pumps for these pastes are often positive displacement pumps, and are pretty much constant torque applications.

Machines

A machine in my definition is something that is built by a machine builder (sometimes called an Original Equipment Manufacturer – OEM) and then shipped, largely complete, to site. This is different from installations, where many machines, drives and electrical systems come together on site.
There aren't so many machines that use pumps, although small pumps apply glue or feed lubrication in many applications. Car washing machines, however, are the exception

A modern car wash contains several pumps and fans. Car wash applications can be difficult, because the installation can be remote (a petrol station in the middle of the desert) and have power supply problems. Also, the detergent and water mixture tends to get everywhere and clog filters, fans and make a mess of the electronics.
Pumps and pump applications are widespread though industry. To finish off with fluid handling, we need to look at a standard industrial workhorse, the compressor.

Compressors

Compressors are sometimes lumped together with pumps and fans, but the business is a bit different. Compressed air is widely used throughout industry as an energy source because it is (pretty) safe, easy to handle, and has no waste product. So most factories have a compressor hidden away somewhere that only gets noticed when it breaks down.
Many compressors operate on a simple stop start control where a pressure switch turns the motor on and off. A better solution is, of course a drive. You are probably familiar with the arguments now. Smoother, more accurate control of pressure. Less mechanical wear from stopping and starting. Energy saving etc. etc. Maybe 25% of new industrial air compressors are now fitted with a drive.
Before we buy our compressor we must look at the application. Most compression processes use oil as a lubricant, and some of this gets into the air. This is a no no in food and beverage, as any contamination (rainbow swirls of oil on your yoghurt?) is unacceptable, so 'oil free' types of compressors are a separate, but significant division in many compressor companies, the other being referred to as 'industrial' or something similar.
Many compressors operate on the same principle of positive displacment pumps (particularly piston and lobe compressors), shown in the figure above. Some other types, including the popular screw compressor, are shown below.

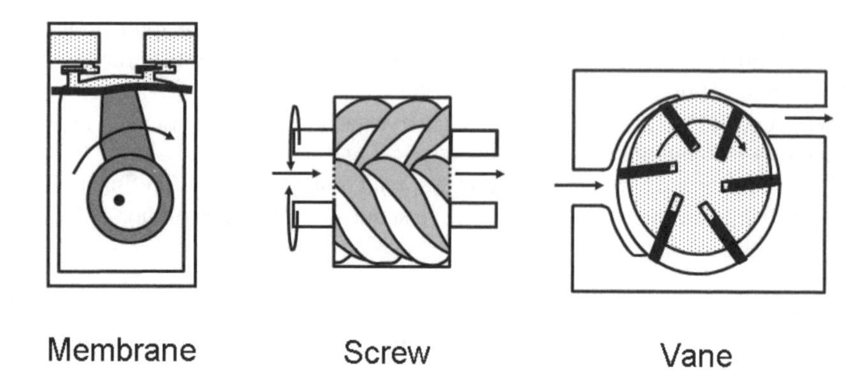

Figure 9.5 Compressors

Piston Compressors (shown earlier) are pretty straightforward to understand, and often have several stages to get a high pressure. Membrane compressors use a flexible membrane instead of a piston and are suited to low volume applications. Screw compressors compress by drawing air into the complex screw pattern, flow being parallel to the axes. There are many variants of vane compressors, which can be oil free; the air flow is at right angles to the axis.

Nearly all the industrial compressors are positive displacement types, and this requirement for constant torque is made worse because, to maintain a good seal, everything is rather tight in a compressor. Also, in types with oil lubrication, the oil can build up in the compression chamber if the compressor has been stopped for some time. So on a cold Monday morning the compressor has practically seized with the cold, and the thick oil has filled the compression chamber, and is not compressible. This needs a lot of starting torque to get going.

Compressors for industrial applications are clearly big business, but air is also compressed for other purposes, medical and diving use for example. At the other end of the pressure spectrum, a vacuum can be produced using similar technology, but by swapping the inlet and outlets around. Compression of other gases is important for storage and distribution. Natural gas is a major fuel source, and compressors to fill the bottles, or the fuel tanks of vehicles, are required in many installations. Drives play a major part in controlling this, because controlling the pressure quickly and accurately will reduce energy consumption considerably.

For the drives supplier, chasing the business of the various compressor manufacturers around the world is a key activity, compressors representing about 5% of the drives business.

Material Handling

Moving away from fans, pumps and compressors, this application is a bit of a catch all. There's conveyers, which vary from big long ones to short, smart ones, as we'll see later. Then there's conveyers for bottles in breweries, and bread in bakeries. Then there are all those pallets, which have to be stacked with material and wrapped in plastic to stop the material falling off. Lifting and lowering with cranes, hoists or just vertical conveyers brings other applications. After pumps, fans and compressors, material handling is the next big drive application. Let's look at conveyers.

Conveyers

I don't know about anyone else, but I split conveyers into bulk handling and item handling applications. Bulk applications usually mean long conveyers, maybe in a quarry or mine, carrying coal or ore. Alternatively, they may be in a factory, carrying sugar, rice, or raw material of some sort. From a drive point of view, they may run virtually continuously, varying their speed to optimise a process by maintaining a steady delivery of material into the furnace or whatever. This can be rather neatly automated in simple systems; See box: **Using Closed Loop Control with Conveyers**.

Using Closed Loop Control with Conveyers

If you are running a process that requires a steady feed of bulk material from a conveyer, you can vary the speed of the conveyer as the density of material on the conveyer varies. Speed up the conveyer if not enough material is coming, slow it down when there is too much. You can automate this. Suppose you are grinding up wood to make fine powder for filling plastics or whatever. If you measure the current in your grinding motor, which may be fixed speed, you can decide if the motor is fully loaded. If it isn't, you can increase the flow of wood bits by speeding up the conveyer that supplies them to the grinder. So if the conveyer is controlled by a small motor and a drive, you can use the drive's internal closed loop controller to keep the main crusher motor current maximum. The setpoint is set in the usual way, and compared with the feedback, the motor current. If the motor current falls, the PID system increases the conveyer speed to add more material, increasing the load current. This simple closed loop control is surprisingly good at optimising a process such as crushing sugar cane or grinding rubber or wood and is shown in the figure below.

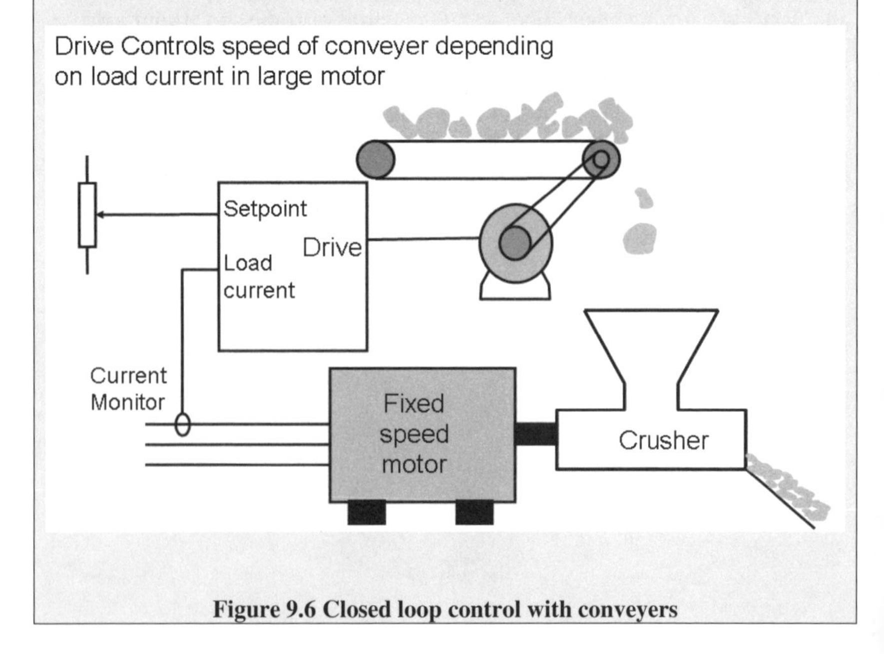

Figure 9.6 Closed loop control with conveyers

With heavy loads on bulk conveyers, starting can be difficult, and can be made worse by the belt sagging between supports, so the material must be lifted a little to get things going. So bulk conveyers are definitely constant torque loads, and may require some starting boost as well as running boost. If the conveyer runs at low speed with high load, cooling of the motor may be a problem. Most of these applications are pretty high power, and may use more than one motor on a belt, requiring some load sharing techniques as described in Chapter 6.

Item Handling

Here we are talking about conveyers that handle individual items that are being sorted or processed. Baggage handling and parcel sorting, or picking and distribution systems in a mail order warehouse are common examples of this. Here the size of the load is not so critical, more important is putting it in the right place at the right time. This will involve many small, short conveyers that could hold one item, and which then switch on when a gap in the main conveyer is detected. You'll see this at some baggage delivery systems in airports, but this is the end of a complex process involving thousands of drives, motors, gearboxes and conveyers. We may joke about lost luggage, but providing the tag stays on the bag, the bar code readers will shunt, shuffle and marshal the bag around the system and deliver it correctly. If this involves diverting the bag to holding areas, additional security systems etc, then the conveyers will be stopped and started accordingly.

Apart from the main conveyers, which move more or less continuously, the small holding conveyers will need to accelerate the bag at the right time to feed it into a gap or whatever. So now we need a high acceleration torque, and we can probably overload the drive and motor, as the conveyer runs for a short time only.

The drive is probably controlled over a serial link, which runs all around the baggage area, and may control hundreds of drives. Similar systems are used for parcel sorting, where the parcels must be directed to the correct dispatch point.

Picking systems, where a customer's order of several items is collected and boxed ready for dispatch are generally easier from a drives point of view as the conveyer timing is less critical.

Figure 9.7 Conveyer Systems

Conveyers in Manufacturing

Conveyers are used at all stages of manufacturing for moving goods. Often the conveyers will move continuously, with speed adjustments to optimise the process. For example, in a packing plant the operator will maybe manually adjust the conveyer speed to supply goods at suitable rate for packing; I saw this used in a very large greenhouse where the tomatoes were supplied on conveyers to a central packing station. As mentioned earlier, often conveyers will bring product to a position, the conveyer will stop while something is done, and then move on. This is how topping is added to pizzas, not by a man with a saucepan and a funny moustache. Where products move from say, a conveyer to a cooling rack, the conveyer must stop and start to transfer the product in the same way as the baggage sorter, so again acceleration and response time is important.
Many conveyers are designed so that the product, for example bottles, can slide freely; the conveyers pushing them gently towards the bottler or labeller or whatever. Soapy water keeps things moving, but beware of the bits of glass that get everywhere!

Conveyer systems usually exhibit a lot of friction, so deceleration does not usually involve regeneration, although if the conveyer is lifting or lowering, that's another matter.

Pallet Handling and Wrapping

Pallets are a good handy way to store and move material, especially bags like cement or fertiliser. The trick is to stack the pallets so they are stable, and wrap them with plastic film to keep the product in place. Automated pallet stackers use conveyers to rotate bags to position them on the pallet. Once the pallet is full, the wrapping is applied by rotating the pallet and unwinding plastic film onto it. You'll need three drives here, one to rotate the pallet, one to move the roll of film up and down to cover the complete pallet, and one to control the tension in the film.

Lifting and lowering; Cranes and hoists

We saw in chapter 3 that an apparently simple application such as a passenger lift can be quite complex for a drive. This is also true for moving goods up and down, whether this is an inclined conveyer, a vertical lifting system, or a crane.

If a conveyer goes up an incline, then as long as we calculate the power needed for lifting and add a healthy allowance for friction and losses, this is no problem. Coming down, we have to be a little more careful. The system may regenerate, and a continuously rated braking resistor may be needed. This is a bit of waste of energy, so if you have other drives nearby, you could connect the DC links together. Now the regenerating drive feeds its energy back to the drive that's motoring, and the braking resistor isn't needed. Be careful though. Are there conditions where both drives can regenerate? Or both motors? How about fusing? Most drives manufacturers will give guidance for this application; we'll see it again when we talk about winding and unwinding; the figure below shows what's happening.

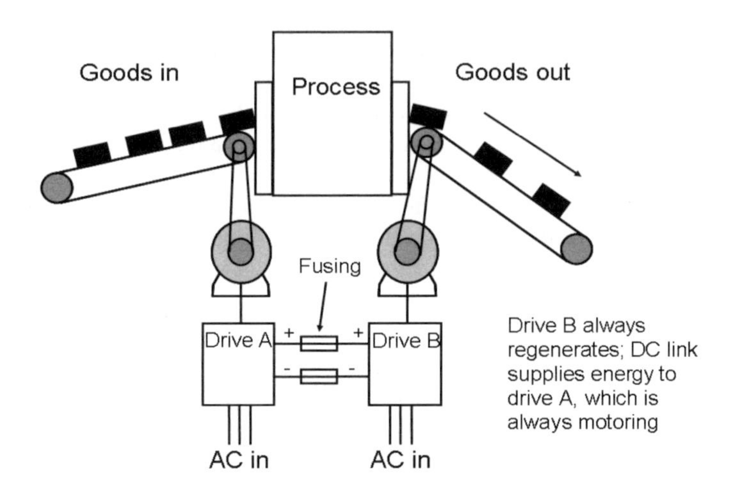

Figure 9.8 Common DC link Application

A vertical conveyer may be just that, with a steady load in one direction, or it may be more like the lift we saw earlier, motoring and generating, forwards and reverse.

Cranes and hoists have similar characteristics and, of course, a technology all of their own. If we are lifting something from the ground, we just need to consider how to get enough torque to start and continue the lift, hopefully without jerking (see chapter 8) the load too much. If we are lowering to the ground, then we need to control the speed so we don't hit the ground too hard.
This is bad enough, but the problems gets harder if we stop the lifting or lowering process halfway, and then have to restart, maybe with an added load. As the brake is released, and the load is hanging in midair, the drive has to supply enough torque immediately to stop the load dropping, and then, really before it starts moving, decide how much torque is needed to lower or lift the load as required. Of course, you'll remember from chapter 8, that speed and torque control is pretty tricky at low speed, and outputting say 3Hz may mean the motor goes forwards if the load is light, or backwards (i.e. with 5Hz slip) if the load is large. If the motor stalls, maybe because the flux is insufficient, the load will fall, and this will please no one.

If we can tolerate a bit of indecision on the drive's part when the brake is released, we can probably manage, but for critical applications like lifts and large cranes, the best solution is an encoder, then the slightest movement either way can be instantly detected and controlled. Some drives, such as vector drives, are able to monitor torque and flux current, and will build the torque before the brake is released. However, I have yet to find a software engineer who will stand under a sixteen ton weight on a crane when the brake is released.

Of course, when you are lowering loads without a counterweight you are regenerating, so a braking resistor is probably needed, although if you have a big system a fully regenerative drive may be a better solution. Cranes are pretty tricky, and many applications are best served by high performance drives. Simple cranes and hoists can easily be handled with relatively simple drives, but encoders ensure smooth and trouble free operation.

Applications in Machines

So far we've talked about the use of drives in large installations and systems, where the drives are mounted in cubicles along with other control equipment, or maybe in a small cabinet in the corner of the factory. However, many drives are built into machines, large and small. A packing machine may use three or four drives to position product, move the wrapping, apply tape etc. A cable manufacturer will be winding and unwinding cable as insulation is applied or cables twisted together. The possibilities are endless, and the advantages of variable speed drives in automation become clear when we look at a few examples. We'll start with some small machines.

Exercise Machines

Not everyone jogs at the same speed, so exercise machines use drives allowing the runner (or walker) to set his or her own pace. Actually this application is quite tricky, because the drive literally sees a step load as a running shoe lands on the moving belt. It is a good application for slip compensation or even vector control to keep the belt speed as constant as possible. There are a surprising number of exercise machine manufacturers, and as this is a 'domestic' application, single phase 230V drives may be preferred, and care must be taken to prevent EMC problems interfering with other systems, such as the television or music system. Running machines usually use motors and drives of 1.5kW or less.

Washing Machines

Most domestic washing machines use simple DC drives for speed control, but for industrial machines AC drives are preferred. A washing machine operates at low speed when washing and, as the clothes tumble, the load can vary, and even regenerate at times. For spin, the drum speed must increase from say from 50 rpm to 1500 rpm so a wide speed range is required from the motor and drive. A standard motor with special bearings will probably allow operation from 10Hz to 300Hz, giving the required speed range. Clearly the low flux at the higher speed means not much torque is available; but this should be OK providing the drum is accelerated slowly. Regeneration can probably be managed with slow deceleration times and maybe a small braking resistor. The drive should be positioned well away from any possible water or foam leaks.

Mixing machine

Cake, chemical or ceramic mix, starting any mixer can be difficult, especially if the mixture has dried a little. Depending on what is being mixed the load will probably increase with speed. A mixer is a good example where maybe only three speeds are required, and a drive is a cheaper and lower maintenance solution compared with a gearbox. If the mixing is automated, speeds can be easily changed and programmed to suit recipes. Mixers don't usually regenerate.

Larger Machines – Plastics

Plastics, as 'The Graduate' was informed, are big business. Raw plastic granules are melted and moulded in various ways to produce the required shapes. Several key processes employ drives:

Extrusion

An extruder squeezes molten plastic out of a shaped nozzle where it solidifies, forming a continuous - er - extrusion. Ideal for making pipes, curtain rails, uPVC window frames, and, if the holes are very small, artificial fibres such as nylon. An extruder uses a pretty big motor to force the molten plastic out. Extruders need high torque continuously, as the plastic should be pretty close to solidifying as it leaves the nozzle. A drive on the motor allows constant pressure to be maintained at the nozzle, giving consistent results. It is not a good idea to position the drive above the extruder, as I once saw, as the heat from the machine causes the drive to overheat.

The blown film extruder is a variant that extrudes thin plastic film, usually from a ring shaped nozzle, to make plastic film, which is then rolled up by – you've guessed it – drives maintaining constant tension. The resulting tube can be further processed to make plastic bags or whatever.

Injection moulding

An injection moulding machine pumps molten plastic into a mould, allows it to set, and then splits the mould to release the product. The more complex the shape, the more splits or 'actions' the mould requires. Some moulding machines operate with hydraulic pressure, developed by a motor driven pump. A drive on the motor will save energy by reducing the speed of the motor at various times in the process, instead of running the motor at full speed and controlling pressure using a relief valve. Big energy savings make retrofitting of drives worthwhile.

Textiles

Textiles are great business, as people always need clothes. Nearly all the processes in the textile industry, from carding to dyeing and printing benefit from a drive, but winding and unwinding of thread is probably the most obvious application. If nothing else, slowly increasing the speed when starting winding a large number of bobbins will reduce breakages, but speed or tension control during running is also useful. When winding bobbins, it's useful to vary the speed slightly to prevent pattern build up on the bobbin. This is known as wobulation, and many drives offer this feature as standard.

Winding and Tension control

Drives are used extensively for winding and unwinding all sorts of threads, cables, textiles, paper, metal film and plate. We've mentioned how it is useful to control tension, and this is often done using a diameter calculator. As material winds up, then the diameter increases, and the torque setpoint (the drive is in torque control) is increased to maintain constant tension (think about it). This calculation, based on the number of turns, thickness of material, pieces of cable per layer (actually not so simple) can be done by some drives.
Alternatively, tension can be measured by a sprung or weighted arm resting on the thread or material, and linked to a potentiometer that feeds a signal back to the drive. This arrangement is called a dancer arm, and is often used in conjunction with the closed loop trim function described in chapter 8.

As the tension increases, the arm is lifted, and the consequent change in feedback voltage from the pot slows the take up drive accordingly, maintaining constant tension.
When winding and unwinding, it is useful, and energy saving, to connect the DC link of the drives together, as described earlier. This way, with the unwinding drive generating (maybe in negative torque control) and the winding drive motoring, there's no need for a braking resistor on the first drive. However, remember only one drive can control the tension!

Packing Machines

Many packing machines use drives to control the transfer of goods in and out of the machine, as well as the packing process, such as folding a box around the goods, or applying polythene wrapping to six packs. Key criteria for drives here is ease of automation – the packing machine will be controlled from a PLC – as well as rapid acceleration and stopping.

Other machines

The list just goes on and on. If you think about it, any automated process benefits from variable speed, either to bring the product to the right place at the right time, to control flow rate or pressure, to save energy, or to optimise the process in some other way. This is why drives are being found in more and more applications in industry, utilities, exercise gyms, and even domestic applications like hot tub baths.
It's not only small machines that use standard drives. Large presses, which have flywheels that provide the energy to press the shape in metal, benefit from drives to bring the flywheel back up to speed in a controlled way. Cement manufacture uses drives to control the grinding and packing process; wire and cables are wound, twisted and unwound many times using drives.

Summary

We've seen how drives are important in fan and pump applications, compressors, material handling and all sorts of machines.
Drives can be used to improve process control, speed things up and slow them down smoothly, control torque and tension, or just save energy. Drive applications will increase as all these benefits become more important, and as new applications arise, new features will be added to drives to make them meet the needs of an ever growing customer base. In particular, increasing interest in energy saving (probably driven by cost and legislation – see chapter 3) will ensure a secure future for drives manufacturers.

10. EMC, Harmonics and Installation

We've hinted several times earlier that drives can cause interference and problems with the supply. We've also mentioned about drives overheating, or failing due to dirt, dust or water getting into them. It's time now to look at these problems in a bit more detail and see how to prevent them causing failure.

Electromagnetic Compatibility (EMC)

If equipment or people are compatible, it means they can work together. EMC is all about equipment not causing interference (sometimes referred to as electromagnetic interference: EMI) with other equipment. As more and more electrical and electronic equipment is installed, EMC control has become an important part of design and system engineering. For example, in the automotive industry, EMC was once only about preventing the ignition systems from interfering with the new fangled radio; in those days people talked about RFI – Radio Frequency Interference. Now vehicle manufacturers have whole departments who have to check complex electronics for internal and external compatibility. Stories of engines cutting out near railway power systems don't help car sales.

The same applies in industrial and domestic applications. As electronics entered factories they encountered an electrically noisy environment, with contactors arcing and unsuppressed relay coils switching. When power electronic systems – usually drives – arrived, they started causing problems themselves as they switched the thyristor current at unheard of speeds. This brings us to the idea that compatibility is a two-way thing. A drive (or anything else) needs to have a certain level of protection against external interference; this is known as its immunity. The drive must also limit the interference that it kicks out – its emissions. So the various committees that deal with these things came up with the concept of the immunity-emissions gap. If all the equipment in a plant has a certain immunity, and all the equipments' emissions are controlled to well below that level, then the 'gap' will represent a safety margin for those that stray a little. The standard levels were set down for Europe in Euronorms, and many other countries then followed suit. These standards were then put into law as a European Directive, and it is now a legal requirement to meet these regulations in Europe.

In case you think this is a little over the top, the stories about EMC problems are legion, and include:

- An antenna for a pager system in a hospital that interfered with patient monitoring.
- Mobile phones causing errors in automated landing systems.
- Failure of warning lights on towers when they are swept by radar from the nearby airport.
- An intermittent short circuit causing transient voltages on a ship, leading to drive failures.
- Drives interfering with sensitive automated weighing systems.
- A DC drive in the next door factory interfering with drives on an assembly machine.
- Noise on the setpoint of a drive causing speed variations.

These days, there are strict regulations concerning EMC in medical applications, and aircraft immunity is greatly improved, but I'll always turn my phone off on the plane.

Drives feature prominently in the list, partly because it is our area of interest, but also because drives are high power, high frequency switching products that appear in industry in large numbers.

The list includes examples where a transmitter of one form or another has been the cause of the problem. There are also examples where the interference has been conducted down the signal or supply cables. Any conductor carrying current produces an electromagnetic field, but at low frequencies the conducted interference is more important. So EMC engineers tend to distinguish between radiated (usually high frequency) and conducted (usually low frequency) interference.

So we can make some crude generalisations:

- High frequency signals (intended or unintended) tend to radiate easily; low frequency signals tend to conduct more easily.
- This effect is also dependent on cable length and frequency. If a cable matches the half wavelength of the signal (or a multiple of this), it will transmit like an antenna.
- If 'go and return' cables are close together, their fields will largely cancel, and radiation will be reduced.
- If a signal source is surrounded by a grounded screen or metal case, the signal is contained. This is known as a Faraday cage (Michael Faraday again).

These rules apply in both directions; that is, a Faraday cage protects from radiated interference; a length of cable will pick up signals at a particular frequency, like an antenna.

From these basic rules, we can start formulating some general rules about limiting interference.

- We can reduce conducted interference using conventional filters. These will limit the interference leaving the drive (emissions) and reduce the interference entering the drive (immunity). Filters are normally used on the mains supply, but motor and signal cables can be filtered if necessary.
- We can limit high frequency interference (emissions and immunity) by careful layout of cables (and pcb tracks) to cancel fields, as well as the use of screening.
- Screening and metal cabinets should be well grounded.

So how do we apply these rules? Well, we apply them when we design the drive, and we apply them when we install it. Of course, these rules apply to all equipment, and should be understood and applied to all equipment and installations to reduce the possibility of EMC problems.

Designing for good EMC

1. Slow down!

The easiest way to reduce the effects of interference is not to produce unwanted signals in the first place. One way to do this is to slow down all the switching you do. Although the switching frequency of our drive may only be 10kHz or so, it produces higher frequencies, because if you analyse any non sinusoidal repetitive waveform (like a PWM square wave) you'll find it contains of lots of multiples of the base frequency, that is - harmonics. A French guy, Fourier, did this analysis so we don't need to. Put another way, you can construct our 10kHz square wave by summing some 10kHz, 20kHz, 30kHz...etc. sine waves of different amplitude together. Actually, the squarer the square wave, the higher frequency harmonics it contains, and we know high frequencies get everywhere. So slowing the switching (rounding the square wave a bit) is great to reduce potential interference problems, but as we know this leads to higher losses in the IGBT (see chapter 2). Compromise is the order of the day.

2. Layout to reduce radiation

If a connection is long and winding, it generates an electromagnetic field, and has a tendency to radiate. If a connection is short, it is less liable to radiate, at least at lower frequencies. If 'go and return' connections are kept close, the fields tend to cancel out, so twisting the cables, or tracking them close on a pcb will help a lot. So pcb layout is all about keeping stuff close together, and making sure tracks don't loop around.

3. Stay close to Ground

For the same reason, keeping a pcb track or cabling close to a grounded conductor will reduce the tendency to radiate. A really good solution here is to use a multilayer pcb with a good, solid ground plane. Not as expensive as it was.

A screen around a cable acts a Faraday cage, providing it is properly grounded. A metal case or cubicle will also eliminate radiated interference, but make sure the door is properly grounded as well, and that ventilation slots are not too large. On many drives with plastic cases you'll see metal straps to ground display panels or control boards to help with EMC.

These precautions reduce the emissions and improve the immunity of a product at the same time. In general, they don't add too much to the cost, and are a lot easier to design in. However, some additional components may also be needed:

4. Filtering out high Frequency

You'll recall from chapter 2 that capacitors have low impedance at high frequency, and inductors have high impedance. So we can fit inductors in series with signals to filter high frequency out, and we can connect capacitors to ground to shunt high frequency away. On the pcb, small, surface mount inductors are often fitted to serial communications connections to limit transients that enter the electronics via these terminals. As previously stated, serial comms cables are often dragged around a factory, where they can pick up all sorts of noise, and if the drives is poorly grounded with respect to the other products on the bus, damaging common mode voltages can result.

Capacitors are sprinkled around more freely, maybe because they are cheaper. A key application for them is on control terminals, where very small capacitors are used to mop up very high frequency noise that can (I know from bitter experience!) interfere with the microprocessor. These capacitors are fitted very close to the terminals, and divert the noise (usually the result of unsuppressed power switching) to a good solid ground plane.

Filtering the control electronics is one thing. The IGBTs are connected to the mains through the rectifiers and the DC link, and it is here where the high switching frequency harmonics generate unwanted interference. We'll need to fit a filter to the supply if we want to have any chance of meeting the standard with any reasonable length of output cable. Why do output cables make a difference? See box: **Working with Long cables**. The filter was described in chapter 7, and is often a factory fitted extra. For additional filtering (for domestic applications for example – see below) an external filter can be purchased and fitted.

Working with Long Cables

When you design a drive, you're probably working on a lab bench with a motor, and if you're lucky, some form of load (like a noisy fan) on the floor blowing air up your trouser leg. When you visit your customer you are rudely surprised to find your lovely drive stuck in a cubicle in a plant room with other equipment, in a dirty hot environment (see later). Where is the motor? It's at the top of the storage silo, maybe 50 or 100 metres away. This matters because the cable from the drive to the motor can act as a transmitter of interference with all those high voltage, pulse width modulated signals in it. But it also matters because the cable has some capacitance to ground. If the cable is screened (and this is recommended to reduce interference) the capacitance is quite high, because the screen is close to the cables, and hopefully grounded. Capacitance to ground and high frequency means current, so quite high, spiky currents can flow. These currents occur during the switching time of the IGBT, increasing losses. Notice we've stopped caring about the interference we may be causing, and are now concerned about overheating our IGBTs. So drive manufacturers will specify a maximum cable length between the drive and the motor. Cable lengths will be shorter for screened (or armoured) cables, but that's no reason to use unscreened and cause interference.
If you must use long cables, (explosive manufacturers still like their electrical systems a long way from the plant for some reason) you can fit inductance in the output, or even fancy filters to round off the switching edges and reduce the current spikes. Typically a drive will work with 50m of screened cable without problems. Reducing the switching frequency can help, but the peak currents are still there, just not so often.

Installing for good EMC

So, hopefully the drive manufacturer has taken care during the design, and has tested his equipment to ensure it meets the legal and market requirements. We now have to install our drive, and make sure our completed machine or installation also minimises emissions and optimises immunity.

Follow some simple rules and you should avoid EMC problems:

1. Ground everything well.
   Of course the drive must be grounded in order for the filters and protection components to be effective, let alone safety. Most manufacturers recommend scraping paint away or using cutting washers to ground the chassis of the drive to a metal backplate as well as any separate terminal connection. Make sure the drive and other equipment is well grounded to a common ground point, using short, thick cable. Why? Well, any length of cable has impedance, the more so at high frequency. So although some lengths of green/yellow (green in US) cabling may be OK for safety grounding, if in practice they are long and thin their impedance will mean a voltage difference between equipment grounds. The ideal cable is a braided (woven) cable that has low impedance at high frequencies. Don't forget to ground the cubicle door as well. Ideally all these ground connections should come to one point, or a copper bus bar somewhere in the cabinet; this will minimise any voltage differences.

2. Use screened or armoured cable for the motor connections, grounding the screen at both ends. This encloses the cable in a Faraday cage, reducing the chance of interference from the switching edges produced by the drive. For signal connections, use screened cable where possible, and certainly for analogue signals and serial communications.

3. Try and keep the power cables and signal cables separate. There's nothing worse than a communications cable in the same cable duct as the connection to the motor, although it still works. Usually.

4. Suppress any inductive loads that are switched within the cubicle, in particular contactor coils. When a relay contact or switch opens and interrupts the current in a coil, the spark acts like a transmitter (Marconi started with spark gaps) and gets into all the wiring, and then into the drive. Use Varistors, flywheel diodes, or ready made Resistor-Capacitor networks.

5. Where screened cables are used, make sure the screens are well grounded where they enter the cubicle (to dump anything they've picked up on the way) and keep the unscreened bits to a minimum – ideally use terminating glands that maintain the screen all the way. Long 'pigtail' end connections, exposing the signal cable are discouraged.

That's enough rules. All this sounds pretty expensive and unnecessary, but it's not so difficult if it is planned from the start. If you have to spend a few days on site trying to fix it, which may mean rewiring a cubicle or fitting suppression on contactors, you'll see how much cheaper it is to do it correctly the first time. EMC engineers always say prevention is better than cure.

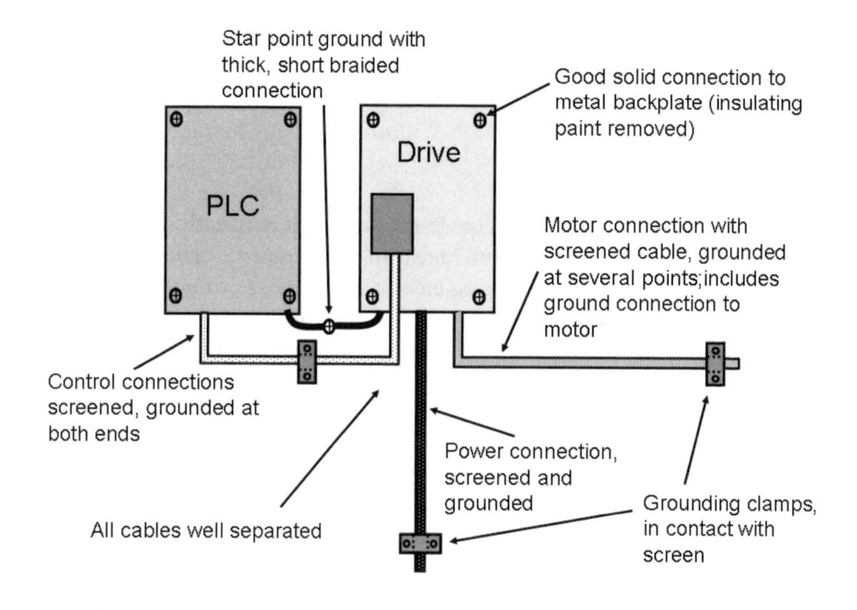

Figure 10.1 Good EMC Installation

Up to now, we've been discussing continuous interference; stuff you can see on a spectrum analyser and puzzle over (where is that 15MHz coming from?). However, included under the heading EMC are the transient events, like voltage spikes on the supply and things.

We've sorted out most of these by adding our various protection components discussed in chapter 7, but let's summarise the possible problems here, as defined in various regulations. Design engineers assume that experts who knew what they are talking about wrote the regulations, and meeting the requirements of the regulations will also meet the requirements of the market. Not always true, but a start.

1. Fast transients. We mentioned earlier how unsuppressed switching of inductive loads (relays and contactors) generates very high frequencies that are conducted and radiated around cubicles. The test usually involves a spark gap to generate a repeatable series of high voltage pulses. These are then connected directly to the supply lines, and hopefully the X and Y capacitors on the input, as well as the Varistors will mop them up. Then the pulses are coupled into the control connections via a screen, and the small inductors and capacitors on the control board mentioned earlier should deal with this, ground planes and good grounding helping as well.

2. High energy transients. These transients are caused by lightning strikes, commutation spikes from DC drives, direct on line motor starts and (very often) unsuppressed switching of banks of capacitors used in many factories for power factor correction. Tests usually involve spikes on the supply of 4kV or more, line to line and line to earth. These can usually be absorbed with varistors and capacitors on the input, but a nice beefy input inductor will reduce their impact as well.

3. Electrostatic discharge. A special 'gun', which will discharge up to 15kV at very low energy onto the drive case and the buttons on the control panel, is used to simulate an operator who has walked across a nylon carpet (in a factory?) and touched the drive. Can happen I guess. Sometimes an extra capacitor or surface mount inductor is added as a result of these tests. It is no longer generally considered funny to use the gun on unsuspecting engineers crouched over computers, but it has brightened up the odd afternoon.

As should be clear by now, international standards define a lot of the levels of emissions and immunity that are required, both for transients and continuous interference described earlier. These regulations are pretty complicated and are defined by reference to other regulations, and have chopped and changed quite a bit. It's made worse by the fact that the actual levels are defined in dBμV, from 150kHz to 1GHz. Briefly, in the past, people used to talk about 'Class A' level, which was industrial, and 'Class B' level, which was domestic. Class A needed a pretty simple filter, class B a bigger one. Now we have C1, C2, C3 and C4 levels, and the situation is complicated by a drives specific standard and requirement, and the fact that it matters whether the equipment is installed by a professional (?) or not. C1 is pretty much domestic and light industrial as before, C2 and C3 levels are industrial, and C4 is for the big stuff. People make a good living as consultants explaining and recommending all this, so the rest of us can have a life. These levels are shown in the figure below.

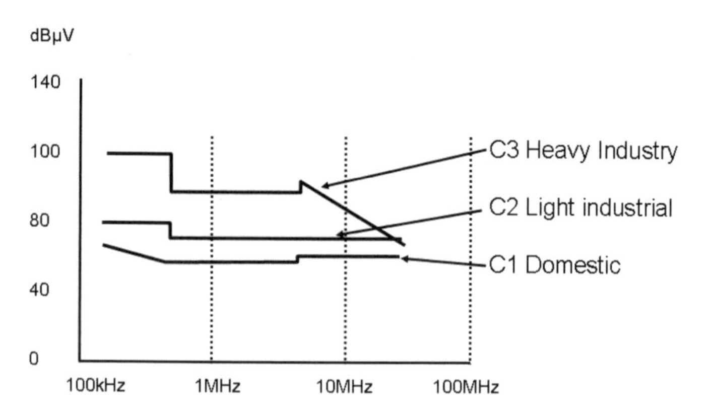

Figure 10.2 Simplified Permitted conducted interference levels

Summary

EMC is pretty important, and should be thought about when designing a drive as well as installing it. If you don't take care, it will probably be OK, but if it goes wrong it gets expensive, you should make sure you have someone else to blame. The same is true for harmonics...

Harmonics

Harmonics are really a special case of EMC. Harmonics (in this context) are the low frequency distortions on the supply voltage or current waveform that can lead to problems. Here we are only concerned with repetitive distortion that can be analysed by Mr Fourier (see earlier; he's a busy guy) and broken down into a series of higher harmonics of the supply frequency. Engineers are always talking about the fifth, seventh harmonic etc. (we'll see why later) but the regulations in Europe now extend to the fiftieth harmonic, which is 2500Hz on a 50Hz supply. Yes, the problem is so bad that there are regulations just like with EMC.

Supply Distortion

We mentioned earlier that sine waves are pretty handy things as they go along transmission lines and through transformers with ease. In the past, loads like motors and incandescent lamps took sine wave currents and all was well. Now electronics has come along with rectifiers and DC links, drawing non-linear currents from the supply. Any impedance in the supply now means the voltage is distorted as well, meaning we have non-sinusoidal waveforms in our supply system. These cause additional losses in transformers and motors, generally upset transmission systems, and may even cause problems with other electronics such as fluorescent lamps and displays. Because most drives just rectify the mains and don't worry about the details of the waveform, drives are usually the troublemakers not the victims here. This problem is getting worse, as more and more power supplies and drives come into use with simple rectifiers. Office blocks in city centres full of PCs are now a major problem for supply authorities. Why the occupants can't work from home I don't know.

Harmonics and their analysis

If we monitor our distorted sine wave and analyse it, we'll use a spectrum analyser or specialist instrument that includes Fourier analysis in its software. This will tell us immediately the levels of the various harmonics that make up the complex waveform. If the load – probably a drive – is a balanced, three phase AC load, there will be no even harmonics (this would mean there is a DC component) and no multiple of three (3rd, 6th 9th etc) because these are balanced out. So the first big harmonics are the 5th and 7th, 250 and 350Hz from a 50Hz supply. As stated above, the regulations in Europe extend to the 50th, but the lower ones generally cause the biggest problems.

Reducing Harmonic Distortion

For installations with new, large drives there is now a standard procedure for analysis of the existing distortion, simulation of the effect of adding the new drives, and checking afterwards that all is well. If the simulation suggests the new drives will cause the installation to exceed permitted harmonic levels, there are several possible solutions:

1. Fitting input inductors. This is the simplest, traditional solution. The inductors smooth out the current peaks in the rectifiers, reducing distortion, at the expense of a few volts on the DC.
2. Harmonic filters. If the simulation suggests the problem lies with a single harmonic – say the 5th, then a series or parallel filter can be fitted that takes out that harmonic. Filters can cause problems such as resonance and other interactions with equipment, but will certainly remove the offending harmonic.
3. Star Delta Transformer. If you have several drives, you can feed some from a star secondary and some from a delta secondary, reducing considerably the harmonics in the supply. The transformer inductance helps as well. A larger drive may be designed with two rectifier bridges for this purpose (like the DC drive in chapter 4). Not cheap though.
4. Active equipment. You can now buy harmonic correction equipment that sits on the supply and sources and sinks current to try to correct the shape of the waveform. You don't need to fully correct the sine wave, just enough to meet the regulations. Just as well; this kit is a lot more expensive than the drives…
5. Drives with smart rectifiers. Some drives offer harmonic control as part of their fully regenerative design using a second inverter in place of the simple rectifier – see chapter 5. This is another expensive option.

The figure below summarises how harmonics are caused, and how they are reduced.

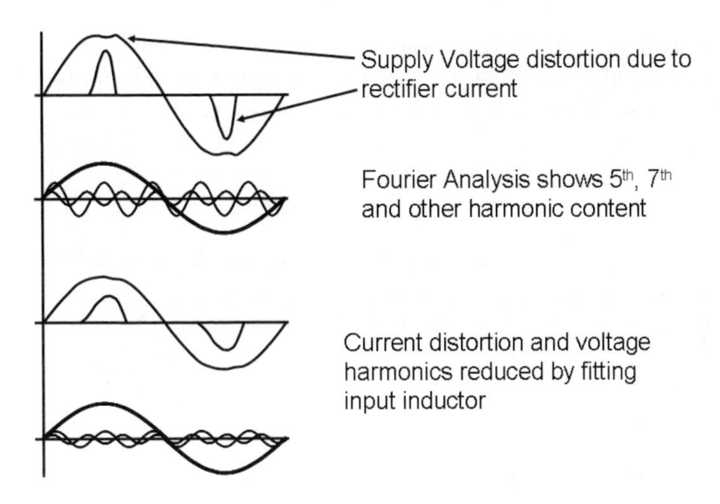

Figure 10.3 Harmonics

Harmonics can be a serious problem with expensive solutions. Luckily, if you are a factory with just a few drives, you'll probably be OK. The regulations don't apply inside the factory, it is the so called point of common coupling, (PCC) where your supply meets other people's that matters.

Most drive manufacturers offer simulation packages so you can calculate the distortion, but some of these are more accurate than others, and some of them tend to be economical with the harmonic levels. After all, if you do a calculation with ABC's package and it looks better than BA's, you're going to buy ABC drives. Also, to get meaningful results you'll need to know quite a bit about supply impedance, information that isn't often easy to get hold of.

Drive designs are changing a little. Reducing the size of the DC link capacitance will reduce distortion, but you need fancy software to cope with supply breaks, transients and regeneration. Adding an inductor in the DC helps a lot, but reduces DC link voltage, adds losses, cost and may be noisy. Harmonics are usually shown in percentage amplitude (compared with the fundamental value) for various harmonic numbers.

The figure below shows typical values up to the 19th harmonic for a standard six pulse rectifer, a six pulse rectifier with a 2% inductor fitted, and a 12 pulse rectifier.

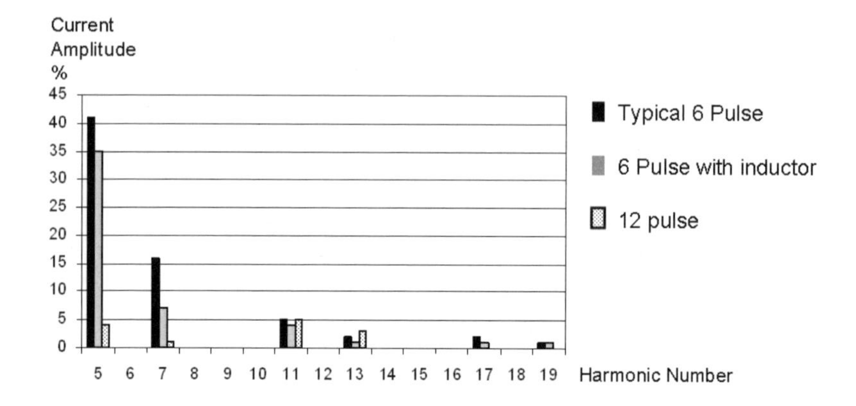

Figure 10.4 Typical Harmonic Values

The answer, as always is to plan ahead, know a bit about your supply and other equipment, and use the simulation packages with care.

Installation

After all this, you still buy a drive and want to install it? OK, but there are a couple of points to take care of even when we've checked the harmonic situation and made our EMC recommendations to the wireman.

Cooling

It should be pretty clear now that we need a supply of cool air to stop the drive overheating. Most drives are specified for a maximum ambient temperature of 50°C, although some of the 'Pump and Fan' variable torque drives may be 40°C maximum. If you fit a drive in a cubicle with other equipment, you'll need to make sure that, when everything is up and running, the inside of the cubicle doesn't exceed this temperature. External fans (with filters?) on the cubicle or even air conditioning units may be needed. If the drive does get too hot, the usual procedure is to open the cubicle doors, and then the dirt and dust from the factory gets in and the drive fails properly – see below.

Altitude affects cooling, because the less air there is, the less cooling effect. Most drives need to be de-rated above 1000m, and once you are high in the Andes in a copper mine, or driving a ski lift in the Alps, this de-rating is significant – 20% or more at 4000m. Usually it's cold up there as well, which helps, but don't rely on it, as the plant room may get quite warm. Some large cities are quite high (Mexico City 2300m, Johannesburg 2000m), so check your atlas if you are exporting.

Dirt, Dust and other Contamination

These are real drive killers. Ever taken the back off of an old television? Full of dust, right? Especially around the high voltage bits! Drives are in an industrial environment, and if you are making, say, steel wire to go into car tyres, there is a fine layer of steel dust everywhere. Flour in bakeries, tiny carbon fibres in a carbon fibre factory, smuts from waste burning; all these have destroyed drives and given air miles to service engineers. Liquids are worse if they get as far as the drive, and we've already mentioned gases like Hydrogen Sulphide in waste water.

The problem is that the dust, conductive or not, seeks out the high voltage stress points and settles there, building up a layer which encourages tracking and breakdown. Clearly conductive dust (like metal or carbon) is a real killer, but non-conducting dust like wood fibre will encourage tracking, especially if it picks up a bit of moisture.

So the user must ensure the cooling air for the drive is clean and filtered, and that drips from pipes or condensation can't get into the drive. Unfortunately, when failure occurs, the manufacturer usually gets the blame and the warranty cost. If you are installing a drive outside of a cubicle, you should think seriously about selecting a unit that has a high degree of protection like IP54 (see chapter 3)

To reduce failures, the designer will try to eliminate high voltage stress points in the drive, and will try make as much space as possible between components at different potential, especially if they are switching at high frequency. See box: **Creepage and Clearance**. They may also try to control the airflow within the drive, for example, by avoiding directing air from the fan over the high voltage electronics to prevent contamination build up. The fans themselves will often fall victim to dirt and dust, slowing or stopping altogether with the consequences you might expect.

Creepage and Clearance

Clearance between live parts at different potential is all about the air gap. Clean, dry air is a pretty good insulator, so air gaps can be pretty small. Creepage, the distance over the surface between parts, is a bit trickier, because any contamination may lead to failure.
There are strict regulations laid down concerning minimum creepage and clearance distances, depending on the operating voltage, the degree of pollution, and the way the product is grounded.
In fact, experience suggests that the distances specified by the regulations may not give the reliability required, and drive designers will try to increase the creepage paths in areas of possible failure. Or more likely, make the necessary changes when a failure pattern becomes evident. These possible points of weakness can be difficult to predict, as cooling airflow may encourage dust flow through the drive, and of course particular points will collect dust in sheltered positions.

Another weapon in the battle against contamination is coating. Conformal coating applies a thick layer of insulating material over the whole pcb and components, and this was often required for military products in the past.

These days, drive manufacturers tend to use a thinner varnish, which is often applied selectively. This makes repair difficult, adds to cost and process time, but certainly increases the reliability of product. Most drives are now coated, at least partially. It doesn't really help if the contamination is very bad.

Summary

So installing and operating the drive is fraught with problems. EMC can prevent correct operation of the drive or other equipment. Harmonics can upset the supply and other users. Dirt, dust, liquids and gases all conspire to destroy the drive. In the end, it's surprising that so many drives and motors perform faultlessly in pretty tough environments around the world. That's electronics for you.

11. Whatever Next?

AC drives are now a mature technology, which means really that the focus in development is to reduce cost and add features, rather than fundamentally change the way the product works. Here we'll just explore some of the factors that will influence what drives in the future will look like, and how and where they are used.

A Growing Market

Picking automation and drives as a career is still a good move. In addition to the factors stated later, the basic need to automate continues to ensure more and more drives and industrial control equipment are sold every year. A growth of about 6% makes a healthy basis to build a successful business. However, that business is scattered throughout the world, and growth is particularly strong in the developing industrial countries, so you'd better have a good export department.

Changing Technologies

OK, it's a mature market, but there are still changes and developments in power electronics and motor control. There is always the possibility of a new power switch to replace the IGBT, but the heady days of the seventies when new devices appeared every year are past. IGBTs have slowly got better over the last twenty years, but no major breakthroughs. Com diodes have also shown improvement, and there is a possibility that Silicon Carbide or similar exotic devices may become cost effective. Silicon Carbide diodes, with no recovered charge, are already used in some high voltage drives, and would greatly improve efficiency. Silicon Carbide transistors have been built, but these are a few years off.

Topology, or the possible configurations of inverters and converters, still contributes to paper mountains and patent lawyers' fees, but again little has changed in industry in the last twenty years. We may see more drives with active front ends (see chapter 5), which save energy and reduce harmonics, and always just over the horizon is the matrix inverter, which offers the philosopher's stone of direct AC to AC conversion. It consists of nine switches in a matrix (hence the imaginative name) and each switch consists of a two IGBTs back to back with blocking diodes included.

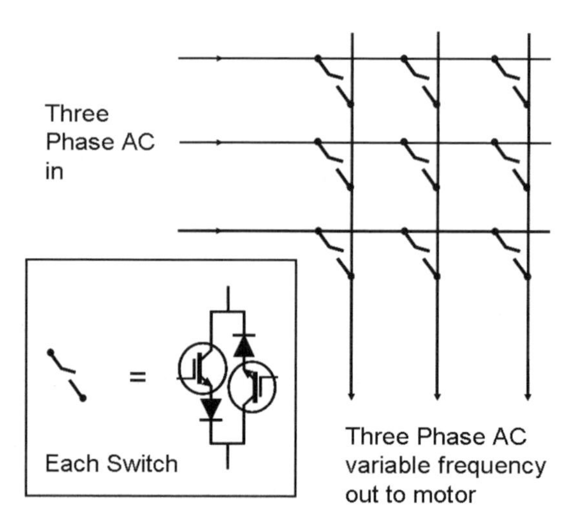

Figure 11.1 Matrix Inverter

Now by cunningly turning on and off IGBTs, a three phase variable voltage, variable frequency waveform can be supplied to the motor as required by picking the appropriate incoming AC phases. No rectifiers, no capacitors. Of course, the matrix can be programmed to control harmonics, regenerate etc. as required. You can see all this takes a lot of software to make this happen. However, there are all sorts of problems getting these things to work, including circulating currents that won't go away, even after the addition of inductors. Also, eighteen IGBTs and diodes are pretty expensive. Nevertheless, it is a possibility and you can now buy one if you want - at a price.

Maybe the main benefit of new technologies will appear in less dramatic ways. It is accepted now that software is full of bugs, and reducing these bugs to a reasonable level is very expensive and time consuming, so automated detection and correction of software is beginning to help. If this becomes efficient and effective, software changes will be quicker and easier and less risky.

Of course, technology has traditionally driven down the price of all electronic goods, so new (aka. faster better cheaper) components and production techniques will continue to do this, particularly in the memory and CPU area of the drive. Passive components appear to be just that; capacitors and inductors are better than they were, but it is difficult to see big changes at the moment.

Quality and Reliability

When AC drives were first developed, they weren't very reliable. The power components were not particularly rugged, and, as we've seen, there was a long, steep, learning curve to climb in order to understand the dirt, dust, temperature, transients and dodgy supplies in the real world of industry. Early software problems didn't help either. Industry responded by taking up the product slowly. But after a while, the designers and component manufacturers got it right, the managers got the credit, and the products improved. So in the last ten years or so the users' viewpoint has changed, and drives are now accepted as just another 'fit and forget' component, and, except for the odd design slip up, drives are pretty reliable. This has further encouraged growth and sales in the business.

Driving the Growth and Development

So what is changing the drives business? What are the expensive market analysis reports telling us? Well, save your money, some of the trends are pretty obvious.

Energy

If they remade "The Graduate" the buzzword would be energy, not plastics. It is difficult to see energy prices falling in the future, and more and more legislation (see chapter 3) is driving energy users to save energy, and therefore money. This can only be a good thing for drives manufacturers, as a drive will nearly always save energy especially, as we saw in chapter 9, when used with pumps and fans. If drive prices fall in real terms (like most electronics, this is the trend) payback times will shorten, and the business can only increase.

Automation and Fieldbus systems

We saw in chapter 8 that features and functions in drives seem to just grow and grow, and there is nothing to stop this continuing. Nothing that is, except the increasing trend to use PLCs and more sophisticated controllers to centralise automation. Most cubicles in a factory now contain a PLC, and very often that PLC is connected to a hierarchical automation system monitoring and controlling the complete factory. Serial communications make this work, and the open standard fieldbus systems (see chapter 8) mean connecting equipment up from different manufacturers is easy. Well, not easy, but possible at least. So the drive becomes a simple power amplifier, without the need for all the features discussed earlier, as the PLC or central control does all the work.

This is a simplification of course. Many drives still use a lot of their built in features while at the end of a fieldbus, and many drives are 'stand alone' controllers or are built into relatively simple machines that don't need serial communications. However, drives are already available that offer open fieldbus systems as standard, and as the price of the interface chips falls, this will continue. Drives are now a part of the technology that is giving us unheated and unlit factories because, for better or worse, there is no-one in them.

Supply Quality, Harmonics and EMC

We saw in chapter 10 that drives manufacturers have met the challenge of EMC legislation, even if customers choose to break the law and fit unfiltered drives. To be fair, most customers and installers now understand these problems, and it is unusual to come across a cubicle that has broken all the EMC rules and recommendations.

However, the next challenge is harmonics, and the rules are tightening up. It may be that the law will force the use of more active front ends, and discussed earlier, or maybe other forms of mitigation may become the norm. But with pressure on energy suppliers to improve efficiency and keep the lights on, harmonics will certainly be one area of interest for drive manufacturers and users.

Final Thoughts

AC drives are a great business to be in. All the exciting technologies in electronics and software are present, the market is growing, and drive manufacturers and users are saving the planet. In industry, processes are improved, energy saved, and some very impressive equipment assembled and operated around the drive.

The drive of the future may look very similar to the drive of today, or it may be very different, but you can be certain there will be a fair number of manufacturers serving a growing number of users for some time to come.

Index